# The *Speedy* Revision Guide

## Key Stage 3
### Tier 4–6

*Speedy* Revision

# Introduction

 This revision guide is aimed at Tier 4–6 of the KS3 National Tests for Mathematics. It's the perfect size to keep with you at all times during the crucial weeks before the tests.

There is *speedy* coverage of each topic in the four main strands:
● Number
● Algebra
● Shape, space & measures
● Handling data

Everything you need to know about a topic is given on one or two pages, in the same format:
● **Essential facts**
   Everything you need to know, complete with examples.
● **Q & A**
   Easy-to-follow worked examples with clearly explained methods.
● **Check-up TESTs**
   To make sure everything has sunk in. (If you can do all the tests, you are heading in the right direction!)

On pages 66–67 there is a *speedy* revision test to check that you have remembered all the basic facts. (If you're short of time, try the revision test first, then revise those topics you got wrong; that truly is *speedy* revision!)

Good luck in your tests!

# Contents

# Special numbers

## ● Even and odd numbers

Even numbers end in 0, 2, 4, 6 or 8 and are exactly divisible by 2.

All other numbers are odd numbers – they end in 1, 3, 5, 7 or 9.

## ● Square numbers

Square numbers are whole numbers multiplied by themselves.

> ➤ **Example**
> '3 squared' is 3 × 3 = 9.
> '3 squared' is written $3^2$.

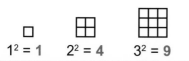

$1^2 = 1$    $2^2 = 4$    $3^2 = 9$    $4^2 = 16$    $5^2 = 25$

## ● Triangular numbers

Start at 1 and add 2, then 3, then 4, ...

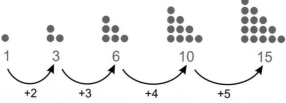

1    3    6    10    15

+2    +3    +4    +5

## ● Prime numbers

A prime number has exactly two factors (itself and 1).

Note: 1 is not a prime number (it has only one factor – itself).

You should memorise the first few primes: 2, 3, 5, 7, 11, 13, 17, ...

Apart from 2, primes are always odd numbers.

Any odd number that's in a times-table other than its own is not a prime number. e.g. 9 is not prime as it's in the 3 times-table.

---

**1** Write down the first ten
  **a** even **b** odd **c** square **d** triangular numbers.
**2** 32, 49, 17, 21, 36, 3, 64
  From the list, write down the
  **a** even **b** odd **c** square **d** triangular **e** prime numbers.

TEST

*Speedy* Revision

# Squares & square roots

## ● Squaring numbers

To square a number, just multiply it by itself.

$4^2$ is shorthand for '4 squared' or '4 × 4'.

Make sure you know all the square numbers up to 12 × 12:

1, 4, 9, 16, 25, 36, 49, 64, 81, 100, 121, 144

> **Examples**
> 1 × 1 = 1
> 2 × 2 = 4
> 3 × 3 = 9
> and so on

### ➤ Q & A

What is $30^2$?

Say this as 'thirty squared'.

**Answer**

| | |
|---|---|
| Write what $30^2$ means: | $30^2 = 30 \times 30$ |
| Write 30 as 3 × 10: | $= 3 \times 10 \times 3 \times 10$ |
| Put the 10s at the end: | $= 3 \times 3 \times 10 \times 10$  (or $3^2 \times 10^2$) |
| Multiply the 3s and the 10s: | $= 9 \times 100$ |
| Finish multiplying: | $= \underline{900}$ |

## ● Square roots

Finding the square root is the opposite of finding the square.

'What is the square root of 16?' means the same as 'What number squared is 16?'

> **Example**
> $\sqrt{16} = 4$
> as 4 × 4 = 16

## ● Powers & roots on your calculator

You should have some buttons like these on your calculator:

$x^2$  $\sqrt{}$

To work out $4^2$ press **4** **$x^2$** **=**. The answer is 16.

To work out $\sqrt{169}$, press **√** **1** **6** **9** **=** or **1** **6** **9** **√**.
The answer is 13. See which works on your calculator.

---

**1** Find these squares: **a** $5^2$ **b** $11^2$ **c** $8^2$ **d** $40^2$

**2** Find these square roots: **a** $\sqrt{36}$ **b** $\sqrt{49}$ **c** $\sqrt{144}$

Check your answers on your calculator.

**TEST**

# Mental strategies for + and –

## ● Partitioning

### ➤ Q & A

**a** 145 + 213  **b** 683 – 274

**Answer**

**a** Re-write the sum with the larger number first:

213 + 145

Add 145 a bit at a time:

213 + 100 + 40 + 5 = 358

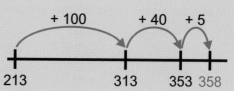

**b** Subtract 274 a bit at a time:

683 – 200 – 70 – 4 = 409

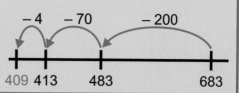

## ● Compensation

> I could do with some compensation.

### ➤ Q & A

**a** 357 + 52  **b** 718 – 496

**Answer**

**a** Round 52 down to 50, then compensate:

357 + 52

= 357 + 50 + 2

= 407 + 2

= 409

**b** Round 496 up to 500, then compensate:

718 – 496

= 718 – 500 + 4

= 218 + 4

= 222

## ● Other useful tricks

Look out for near doubles:  150 + 160 = double 150 + 10 = 310

Find pairs totalling 10:  9 + 7 + 1 + 3 = 9 + 1 + 7 + 3 = 10 + 10 = 20

---

**1** Use partitioning to answer these:
  **a** 418 + 67  **b** 112 + 375  **c** 893 – 46  **d** 510 – 146

**2** Use compensation to answer these:
  **a** 58 + 73  **b** 346 + 207  **c** 489 – 64  **d** 782 – 517

TEST

**Speedy** Revision

# Written methods for + and –

## ● Whole numbers

### ➤ Q & A

**a** 139 + 57

**b** 723 – 382

Answer

Answer

**a**

```
  1 3 9
+   5 7
  1 9 6
  1
```

9 + 7 = 16

Carry the '1' to
the tens column.

> ### ➤ Method
> ❶ Line up the units.
> ❷ Add/subtract the units first.
> ❸ Then tens, then hundreds.

**b**

```
  ⁶7̶¹2 3
–  3 8 2
   3 4 1
```

2 is less than 8
so 'borrow' a ten.
12 – 8 = 4

## ● Decimals

### ➤ Q & A

**a** 4.72 + 3.51

**b** 57.3 – 1.28

Answer

Answer

**a**

```
  4 . 7 2
+ 3 . 5 1
  8 . 2 3
  1
```

7 + 5 = 12

Carry the '1' to the
units column.

> ### ➤ Method
> ❶ Line up the units.
> ❷ Add/subtract a column at a time, starting on the <u>right</u>.

**b**

Add a zero
place holder.

```
  5 7 . ²3̶¹0
–    1 . 2 8
  5 6 . 0 2
```

0 is less than 8
so 'borrow' from
the next column.
10 – 8 = 2

---

**1** Use a written method to calculate:
   **a** 251 + 143   **b** 591 + 286   **c** 579 – 141   **d** 1703 – 92

**2** Use a written method to calculate:
   **a** 5.16 + 2.73   **b** 1.49 + 2.35   **c** 2.3 – 2.14   **d** 171.54 – 5.71

TEST

# Multiplying & dividing by 10, 100, 1000, ...

## ● Multiplying by 10, 100 or 1000

To multiply by:

| | Th | H | T | U |
|---|---|---|---|---|
| | | | 3 | 7 |

10 move the digits <u>1 place left</u>      37 × 10 =    3 7 0

100 move the digits <u>2 places left</u>    37 × 100 =   3 7 0 0

1000 move the digits <u>3 places left</u>   37 × 1000 = 3 7 0 0 0

## ● Dividing by 10, 100 or 1000

To divide by:

| | Th | H | T | U |
|---|---|---|---|---|
| | 4 | 0 | 0 | 0 |

10 move the digits <u>1 place right</u>      4000 ÷ 10 =    4 0 0

100 move the digits <u>2 places right</u>    4000 ÷ 100 =     4 0

1000 move the digits <u>3 places right</u>   4000 ÷ 1000 =      4

You can apply the above methods to <u>decimals</u>. You can also extend to multiplying and dividing by <u>multiples</u> such as 40, 300 and 7000.

### ► Q & A

Work out:   **a**   1.8 × 100   **b**   1.8 ÷ 10   **c**   12 × 300   **d**   160 ÷ 40

**Answer**

**a**   Multiplying by 100 so move the digits 2 places to the left:
     1.8 × 100 = <u>180</u>

**b**   Dividing by 10 so move the digits 1 place to the right:
     1.8 ÷ 10 = <u>0.18</u>

**c**   To multiply by 300, first multiply by 3 and then multiply by 100:
     12 × 3 = 36;   36 × 100 = <u>3600</u> (move digits 2 places left).

**d**   To divide by 40, first divide by 4 and then divide by 10:
     160 ÷ 4 = 40;   40 ÷ 10 = <u>4</u> (move digits 1 place right).

| | | | | | |
|---|---|---|---|---|---|
| **1**   **a**   39 × 10 | **b**   8 × 1000 | **c**   7.1 × 10 | **d**   1.5 × 100 | |
|     **e**   420 ÷ 10 | **f**   6400 ÷ 100 | **g**   16.3 ÷ 10 | **h**   149 ÷ 100 | |
| **2**   **a**   2.4 × 1000 | **b**   2.4 ÷ 100 | **c**   21 × 4000 | **d**   210 ÷ 300 | |

**TEST**

# Mental strategies for × and ÷

## ● Strategies for multiplying

To multiply by 4, double then double again.

To multiply by 5, multiply by 10 then halve.

To multiply by 9, multiply by 10 then subtract the original number.

To multiply by 11, multiply by 10 then add the original number.

To multiply by 19, multiply by 20 then subtract the original number.

To multiply by 20, multiply by 10 then double.

To multiply by 21, multiply by 20 then add the original number.

To multiply by 25, multiply by 100 then divide by 4.

To multiply by 49, multiply by 50 then subtract the original number.

To multiply by 50, multiply by 100 then halve.

To multiply by 51, multiply by 50 then add the original number.

## ● Partitioning a multiplication

$15 \times 7$ means '15 lots of 7'.

Because 15 is $10 + 5$, you can split '15 lots of 7' into '10 lots of 7' and '5 lots of 7'.

### ➤ Q & A

Calculate $15 \times 7$.

**Answer**

$10 \times 7 = 70$

$+ \underline{\ 5 \times 7 = \ 35}$   [to multiply by 5, multiply by 10 then halve]

$15 \times 7 = \underline{105}$

## ● Using times-tables to divide

'Work out $27 \div 9$' means the same as '$9 \times ? = 27$'.

You know from your times-tables that $9 \times 3 = 27$, so $27 \div 9 = 3$.

---

Do these questions mentally.

1 Calculate: **a** $14 \times 4$ **b** $23 \times 9$ **c** $110 \times 7$ **d** $17 \times 12$

2 Work out: **a** $56 \div 8$ **b** $72 \div 9$ **c** $121 \div 11$

TEST

# Written multiplication

## ● Grid method

### ➤ Q & A
Use the grid method to work out 29 × 42.

**Answer**

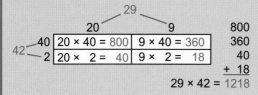

|       | 20            | 9             |     |
|-------|---------------|---------------|-----|
| 40    | 20 × 40 = 800 | 9 × 40 = 360  | 800 |
| 2     | 20 × 2 = 40   | 9 × 2 = 18    | 360 |
|       |               |               | 40  |
|       |               |               | + 18 |

29 × 42 = 1218

### ➤ Method
❶ Split 29 and 42 into tens and units.
❷ Multiply top number by side number in each box.
❸ Add the four products.

## ● Column method
If you prefer, you can use the column method for multiplying numbers like 52 × 17.

### ➤ Example
$$
\begin{array}{r}
52 \\
\times\ 17 \\
\end{array}
$$
52 × 10 = 520
52 × 7 = + 364
52 × 17 = 884

## ● Multiplying a decimal
If one of the numbers is a decimal, you can still use the grid method or the column method.

### ➤ Q & A
Work out 7.18 × 9.

**Answer**

Grid method:

7.18 = 7 + 0.1 + 0.08

| ×   | 7          | 0.1         | 0.08          |
|-----|------------|-------------|---------------|
| 9   | 7 × 9 = 63 | 0.1 × 9 = 0.9 | 0.08 × 9 = 0.72 |

63 + 0.9 + 0.72 = 64.62

Column method:

Find 718 × 9 then divide by 100.

7.18 × 9 = 718 × 9 ÷ 100

$$
\begin{array}{r}
718 \\
\times\ 9 \\
\end{array}
$$
700 × 9 = 6300
10 × 9 = 90
8 × 9 = + 72
718 × 9 = 6462 —÷100→ 64.62

---

**1** Use the grid method: **a** 36 × 23 **b** 121 × 14 **c** 6.42 × 7
**2** Check your answers to **Q1** using the column method.

TEST

# Written division

## ● Whole numbers

Keep taking off multiples of the divisor (the number you're dividing by) until you can't subtract any more.

Then add the 'lots' you used.
So if you took off <u>10</u> lots and <u>7</u> lots, the answer is <u>10 + 7 = 17</u>.

> ### ➤ Example
>
> 136 ÷ 8
>
> ```
> 8 ) 136
>    − 80    10 × 8
>      56
>    − 56    7 × 8
>       0
> ```
> Answer = <u>17</u>

## ● Remainders

Sometimes you will not be able to get to zero, and you will have to give a remainder as part of the answer.

### ➤ Q & A

Work out 452 ÷ 6.

**Answer**

```
6 ) 452
   − 420    70 × 6
     32
   − 30     5 × 6
      2
```

2 < 6, so you can't take off any more 6s.

Answer = 75 remainder 2

## ● Decimals

The method is the same as for whole numbers, but make sure you keep the decimal points lined up.

Write 70.0 rather than 70 to help you keep everything in columns.

There is no remainder this time.

> ### ➤ Example
>
> 105.7 ÷ 7
>
> ```
> 7 ) 105.7
>    − 70.0    10 × 7
>      35.7
>    − 35.0    5 × 7
>       0.7
>    −  0.7    0.1 × 7
>       0.0
> ```
> Answer = <u>15.1</u>

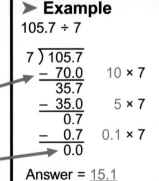

---

**1** Work out: **a** 112 ÷ 7  **b** 207 ÷ 9  **c** 118 ÷ 6

**2** Work out: **a** 63.5 ÷ 5  **b** 120.6 ÷ 9  **c** 237.6 ÷ 11

TEST

# Multiples, factors & prime factors

## ● Multiples

The <u>multiples</u> of a number are the numbers in its <u>times-table</u>.

### ➤ Example

The 3 times-table is:

$1 \times 3 = 3$, $2 \times 3 = 6$, $3 \times 3 = 9$ ...

The multiples of 3 are: 3, 6, 9, ...

## ● Factors

The <u>factors</u> of a number are the numbers that <u>divide into it exactly</u> (including 1 and itself).

You can use these tests to find out the factors of a number:

If it is <u>even</u>, then <u>2 is a factor</u>. (Even numbers end in 0, 2, 4, 6 or 8.)

If the <u>sum of the digits</u> is a <u>multiple of 3</u>, then <u>3 is a factor</u>.

If the <u>sum of the digits</u> is a <u>multiple of 9</u>, then <u>9 is a factor</u>.

If <u>half</u> the number is an <u>even number</u>, then <u>4 is a factor</u>.

If it <u>ends in 0 or 5</u>, then <u>5 is a factor</u>.

If it <u>ends in 0</u>, then <u>10 is a factor</u>.

## ➤ Q & A

Are 2, 3, 4, 5 and 10 factors of 310?

**Answer**

310 ends in 0, so <u>2, 5 and 10 are factors</u>.

$3 + 1 + 0 = 4$ which is not a multiple of 3, so <u>3 is not a factor</u>.

Half 310 = 155 which is odd, so <u>4 is not a factor</u>.

## ● Prime factors

Prime numbers that are factors of a number are called <u>prime factors</u>. For example, 3 is a prime factor of 15 (3 is prime and a factor of 15). You can write any number as a <u>product of its prime factors</u>:

➤ $20 = 4 \times 5 = 2 \times 2 \times 5 = 2^2 \times 5$

Break 20 into 4 × 5. Break 4 into 2 × 2. Only primes left. Re-write the answer with indices.

---

1  List the first five multiples of these: **a** 5 **b** 8 **c** 6 **d** 9
2  List all the factors of these: **a** 8 **b** 32 **c** 40
3  Write these as products of their prime factors: **a** 36 **b** 84

TEST

*Speedy* Revision

# LCM & HCF

## ● Least common multiple

The <u>least common multiple</u> (LCM) is the <u>smallest</u> number that is a <u>multiple</u> of all the numbers in question.

### ➤ Q & A

What is the LCM of 4 and 14?

**Answer**

### ➤ Method
❶ List the <u>multiples</u> of both numbers.
❷ Pick out the <u>smallest</u> number that's in both lists.

List the multiples of the numbers:
Multiples of 4 are 4, 8, 12, 16, 20, 24, <u>28</u>, 32, ...
Multiples of 14 are 14, <u>28</u>, 42, ...

The smallest number that's in both lists is 28, so <u>28 is the LCM of 4 and 14</u>.

Note: '<u>least</u> common multiple' is the same thing as '<u>lowest</u> common multiple'. Some people prefer lowest, some least – luckily they both shorten to LCM.

## ● Highest common factor

The <u>highest common factor</u> (HCF) is the <u>largest</u> number that is a <u>factor</u> of all the numbers in question.

### ➤ Q & A

What is the HCF of 24 and 36?

**Answer**

### ➤ Method
❶ List the <u>factors</u> of both numbers.
❷ Pick out the <u>largest</u> number that's in both lists.

List the factors of the numbers:
Factors of 24 are 1, 2, 3, 4, 6, 8, <u>12</u>, 24
Factors of 36 are 1, 2, 3, 4, 6, 9, <u>12</u>, 18, 36

The largest number that's in both lists is <u>12</u>, so <u>12 is the HCF of 24 and 36</u>.

Write down all your working.

**1** What is the LCM of **a** 6 and 8 **b** 16 and 36?
**2** What is the HCF of **a** 4 and 16 **b** 21 and 35?

TEST

# Ordering numbers

## ● Symbols you should know

= means 'is equal to'

< means 'is less than', e.g. 3 < 4

> means 'is greater than', e.g. 4 > 3

≤ means 'is less than or equal to'

≥ means 'is greater than or equal to'

> ### ➤ Example
> If 13 016 ≤ ☐ ≤ 13 599 then 13 016 could go in the box, or 13 599, or any number in between.

## ● In the middle

Use a number line to find the number halfway between 2 numbers.

The number halfway between 18 940 and 18 950 is 18 945.

18 940     18 945     18 950

## ● Ordering whole numbers

### ➤ Q & A

Put these in order, smallest first:
999, 2012, 1998, 152, 56, 4162

**Answer**

2-digits   3-digits     4-digits

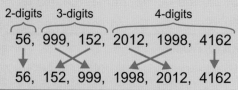

56, 999, 152, 2012, 1998, 4162

56, 152, 999, 1998, 2012, 4162

> ### ➤ Method
> ❶ Write any 1-digit numbers first, then 2-digit numbers, then 3-digit numbers, ...
> ❷ Put each group in order.

## ● Ordering decimals

To find out whether 4.16 is greater than 4.128, write them underneath each other, with the decimal points lined up.

Compare the digits in the first column <u>from the left</u> where the digits are <u>not the same</u>.

$$4 . 1 \,\fbox{6}$$
$$4 . 1 \,\fbox{2} 8$$

same   same

6 > 2

<u>6</u> > <u>2</u> so 4.1<u>6</u> > 4.1<u>2</u>8

---

**1**   Find the number halfway between 34 000 and 34 600.

**2**   Put in order, smallest first: 516, 209, 33, 1460, 888

**3**   Which is greater, 23.19 or 23.25?

TEST

14

# Rounding & estimating (1)

## ● Rounding to the nearest 10

To round 8632 to the nearest 10 you need to decide whether it is closer to 8630 or 8640.

Sketch a number line to find out.

8632 is closer to 8630.
8632 is <u>8630</u> to the nearest 10.

For numbers that are <u>exactly halfway</u>, always <u>round up</u>.

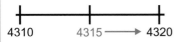

4315 is exactly halfway between 4310 and 4320.
So 4315 is <u>4320</u> to the nearest 10.

## ● Rounding to the nearest 100 or 1000

### ➤ Q & A

Round **a** 8350 to the nearest 100 **b** 6790 to the nearest 1000.

**Answer**

**a** 8350 is between 8300 and 8400.
It is exactly halfway.
So 8350 is <u>8400</u> to the nearest 100.

**b** 6790 is between 6000 and 7000.
It is closest to 7000.
So 6790 is <u>7000</u> to the nearest 1000.

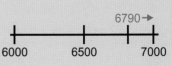

## ● Estimating calculations

Always check answers to calculations by estimating.

For example, 519 + 34 is roughly 520 + 30 = 550.

Now use 'compensation' (page 6) to find the exact answer. Go on!

*Always make an estimate*

You should get 553, which is close to 550, so you can be confident you haven't made a ridiculous mistake.

---

**1** Round to the nearest 10: **a** 79 **b** 435 **c** 1067
**2** Round to the nearest 1000: **a** 1051 **b** 500 **c** 16 800
**3** Do you think 489 + 204 = 936 is correct? Explain.

TEST

# Rounding & estimating (2)

## ● Rounding to the nearest whole number

You don't have to draw a number line to see whether to round a number up or down.

To round to the nearest whole number, look at the <u>tenths digit</u>.
If it is <u>less than 5</u> you <u>round down</u>.
If it is <u>5 or more</u> you <u>round up</u>.

➤ **Examples**
In 6.<u>2</u> the tenths digit is 2.
2 < 5 so round down to 6.
In 6.<u>5</u> the tenths digit is 5.
5 ≥ 5 so round up to 7.

You can still see this on a number line:

## ● Rounding to one decimal place (1 d.p.)

Rounding to 1 d.p. means rounding to the <u>nearest tenth</u>.

To see whether to round to the tenth above or below, look at the next place – the hundredths digit.

➤ 3.2<u>7</u> has 7 in the next place.
7 ≥ 5 so round up.
3.27 is <u>3.3 to 1 d.p.</u>

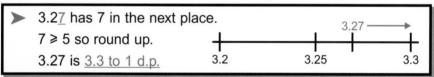

Note: 2.98 is 3.0 to 1 d.p. <u>not</u> 3.
The zero shows it is to 1 d.p. not to the nearest whole number.

## ● Rounding to two decimal places (2 d.p.)

Rounding to 2 d.p. is very similar to rounding to 1 d.p.
But in this case you look at the <u>thousandths</u> digit (3rd decimal place) to see whether to round up or down:

➤ In 3.23<u>8</u>453 the thousandths digit is 8.
8 ≥ 5 so round up. 3.238453 is <u>3.24 to 2 d.p.</u>

---

**TEST**

1 Round to the nearest whole number: **a** 7.6 **b** 3.16 **c** 4.99
2 Round these to 1 d.p. **a** 4.61 **b** 6.45 **c** 1.32 **d** 3.97
3 Round these to 2 d.p. **a** 4.614 **b** 6.458 **c** 1.3248 **d** 3.999

*Speedy* Revision

# Negative numbers

## ● Temperatures on a thermometer

Temperatures on a thermometer can be positive or negative.

Numbers <u>more than 0</u> are <u>positive numbers</u>.
e.g. 5, 10, ...

Numbers <u>less than 0</u> are <u>negative numbers</u>.
e.g. –5, –10, ...

–10°C is <u>less than</u> –5°C, as it is <u>lower down</u> the thermometer.
You can write this as –10 < –5.

Numbers getting bigger: temperatures getting hotter.

Numbers getting smaller: temperatures getting colder.

---

## ● Ordering negative numbers

You can order these:

–2, 3, 1, –4, 5

on a number line.

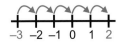

In order, smallest first: –4, –2, 1, 3, 5

---

## ● Adding & subtracting negative numbers

Count <u>on</u> when you <u>add</u>.

–3 + 5 = 2

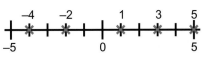

–3 –2 –1 0 1 2

Start at –3 and go on 5.

Count <u>back</u> when you <u>subtract</u>.

–1 – 7 = –8

–8 –7 –6 –5 –4 –3 –2 –1

Start at –1 and go back 7.

---

**1** Look at the thermometer. Which is smaller, 5 or –10?

**2** Put these in order, smallest first: 2, 0, –4, –5, 3

**3** Show on a number line: **a** –8 + 3 **b** –2 – 3

TEST

# Fractions (1)

A fraction shows the number of parts out of the whole.

The top is the numerator. → **3** ← 3 parts are shaded ...

The bottom is the denominator. → **5** ← ... out of 5

► **Example**

$\frac{3}{5}$ is three-fifths.

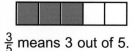

$\frac{3}{5}$ means 3 out of 5.

## ● Equivalent fractions

Equivalent fractions look the same.

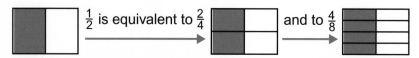

$\frac{1}{2}$ is equivalent to $\frac{2}{4}$ and to $\frac{4}{8}$

You can find <u>equivalent fractions</u> by <u>multiplying or dividing</u> top and bottom (numerator and denominator) by the <u>same number</u>.

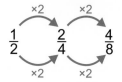

$$\frac{1}{2} \quad \frac{2}{4} \quad \frac{4}{8}$$

×2   ×2
×2   ×2

## ● Simplifying fractions

To simplify a fraction <u>divide</u> top and bottom by the same number. If you can't divide any more you have the <u>simplest form</u>.

► **Q & A**

Write $\frac{15}{45}$ in its simplest form.

**Answer**

Divide by 5: $\frac{15}{45} = \frac{3}{9}$    then divide by 3: $\frac{3}{9} = \frac{1}{3}$

÷5       ÷3
÷5       ÷3

You can't divide any more, so $\frac{1}{3}$ is the simplest form.

---

**1** Write down the fraction that is shaded:

**2** Write as a fraction in its simplest form:

   **a** $\frac{4}{6}$   **b** $\frac{12}{16}$   **c** 4p out of 10p (Hint: 10 parts worth 1p each)

**TEST**

18

# Fractions (2)

## ● Adding fractions

You can only add fractions if they have the _same denominator_.

You add them by _adding the numerators_.

Remember:
The numerator is the top.
The denominator is the bottom.

### ➤ Q & A

Work out $\frac{2}{9} + \frac{1}{9} + \frac{1}{9}$.

**Answer**

$\frac{2}{9} + \frac{1}{9} + \frac{1}{9}$

$= \frac{2+1+1}{9}$

$= \frac{4}{9}$

## ● Subtracting fractions

You can only subtract fractions if they have the _same denominator_.

You subtract them by _subtracting the numerators_.

### ➤ Q & A

Work out $\frac{7}{8} - \frac{3}{4}$. Give your answer in its simplest form.

**Answer**

You need to first write both fractions with the same denominator.

$\frac{7}{8} - \frac{3}{4} = \frac{7}{8} - \frac{6}{8}$ ⟵    $\frac{3}{4} \overset{\times 2}{\underset{\times 2}{=}} \frac{6}{8}$

$\qquad = \frac{7-6}{8}$

$\qquad = \frac{1}{8}$

---

**1** a $\frac{1}{7} + \frac{1}{7}$    b $\frac{1}{5} + \frac{1}{5} + \frac{1}{5}$    c $\frac{2}{9} + \frac{2}{3}$

**2** a $\frac{8}{9} - \frac{3}{9}$    b $\frac{2}{5} + \frac{1}{5} - \frac{1}{5}$    c $\frac{3}{4} + \frac{5}{8} - \frac{3}{8}$

**3** Calculate $\frac{7}{10} + \frac{3}{10} - \frac{6}{10}$. Simplify your answer.

TEST

# Fractions (3)

## ● Improper & mixed fractions

Improper fractions are 'top heavy', i.e. the numerator is bigger than the denominator.

Mixed numbers are made up of a whole number and a fraction.

### ➤ Q & A

**a** Write $2\frac{1}{4}$ as an improper fraction.

**b** Write $\frac{5}{2}$ as a mixed number.

**Answer**

**a** $2\frac{1}{4} = 1 + 1 + \frac{1}{4}$

$= \frac{4}{4} + \frac{4}{4} + \frac{1}{4}$

$= \frac{4 + 4 + 1}{4}$

$= \frac{9}{4}$

**b** $\frac{5}{2} = \frac{2 + 2 + 1}{2}$

$= \frac{2}{2} + \frac{2}{2} + \frac{1}{2}$

$= 1 + 1 + \frac{1}{2}$

$= 2\frac{1}{2}$

## ● Ordering fractions

Ordering fractions is easy if you re-write them with the same denominator; you then just compare the numerators.

### ➤ Q & A

Put these in order, smallest first: $\frac{3}{4}$, $\frac{4}{6}$, $\frac{7}{12}$

**Answer**

All the fractions can be written with 12 as a denominator (this is because 12 is a multiple of 4, 6 and 12).

$\frac{3}{4} = \frac{9}{12}$ ×3     $\frac{4}{6} = \frac{8}{12}$ ×2

$\frac{7}{12} < \frac{8}{12} < \frac{9}{12}$, so the correct order is:

$\frac{7}{12}$, $\frac{4}{6}$, $\frac{3}{4}$

---

**1** Write $1\frac{2}{3}$ as an improper fraction.

**2** Write $\frac{10}{3}$ as a mixed number.

**3** Put in order, smallest first: $\frac{7}{8}$ $\frac{1}{2}$ $\frac{3}{4}$

TEST

*Speedy* Revision

# Fractions (4)

## ● Multiplying fractions

You <u>multiply the numerators</u>, then you <u>multiply the denominators</u>.

> ### ➤ Example
>
> $$\frac{3}{4} \times \frac{5}{7} = \frac{3 \times 5}{4 \times 7} = \frac{15}{28}$$

Sometimes you can <u>cancel out common factors</u> to make the multiplication easier:

> ### ➤ Example
>
> $$\frac{9}{10} \times \frac{15}{36} = \frac{\overset{1}{9}}{10} \times \frac{15}{36} = \frac{\overset{1}{9}}{10} \times \frac{\overset{3}{15}}{36} = \frac{1 \times 3}{2 \times 4} = \frac{3}{8}$$
>
> 9 is a common factor of 9 and 36, so you can cancel these out (there is 1 nine in 9 and 4 nines in 36).
>
> 5 is a common factor of 10 and 15, so you can cancel these out (there are 2 fives in 10 and 3 fives in 15).

## ● Dividing fractions

To divide fractions, you turn the <u>second one over and then multiply</u>.

> ### ➤ Example
>
> $$\frac{2}{9} \div \frac{3}{7} = \frac{2}{9} \times \frac{7}{3} = \frac{2 \times 7}{9 \times 3} = \frac{14}{27}$$

## ● Fraction of

To find <u>one-third</u> of something you divide by <u>three</u>.

To find <u>two-thirds</u>, you <u>find a third</u> then <u>multiply by two</u>.

You can find other fractions exactly the same way – find one part then multiply.

> ### ➤ Example
>
> $\frac{1}{3}$ of £60 = £60 ÷ 3 = £20
>
> ↓×2          ↓×2
>
> $\frac{2}{3}$ of £60 = £20 × 2 = £40

## ● Fractions on your calculator

Your calculator should have a button that looks like **a b/c**.

To work out $\frac{2}{9} \div \frac{3}{7}$ press **2** **a b/c** **9** **÷** **3** **a b/c** **7** **=** to get

⌐ 14⌐27 ⌐ in your display. This means the answer is $\frac{14}{27}$.

---

**1 a** $\frac{5}{7} \times \frac{2}{7}$  **b** $\frac{6}{8} \times \frac{8}{9}$  **c** $\frac{2}{9} \div \frac{2}{3}$  **d** $\frac{4}{7} \div \frac{8}{9}$  **e** Find $\frac{2}{5}$ of £55.

**2** Check your answers to **Q1** on a calculator.

**TEST**

# Percentages

## ● 'Per cent' means 'out of 100'

So '10 per cent' means '10 out of 100'.

$$10\% = \frac{10}{100} \text{ or } \frac{1}{10}$$

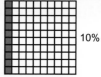

10%

The % symbol can be used in place of the words 'per cent'.

## ● Express a number as a percentage of another

### ➤ Q & A

Express £26 as a percentage of £40.

Answer

26 ÷ 40 = 0.65

0.65 × 100% = 65%

### ➤ Method

❶ Divide the first number by the second number.

❷ Multiply by 100%.

## ● Percentage of

### ➤ Q & A

Find 20% of £400.

Answer

1% is £400 ÷ 100 = £4

20% is £4 × 20 = £80

### ➤ Method

❶ Divide by 100 to find 1%.

❷ Multiply by the number of per cent required.

## ● Percentage increase/decrease

### ➤ Q & A

Increase £20 by 17.5%.

Answer

1% is £20 ÷ 100 = £0.20.

17.5% is £0.20 × 17.5 = £3.50

(this is the increase).

The answer is £20 + £3.50 = £23.50.

### ➤ Method

❶ Find the increase (or decrease).

❷ Add it to the price. (Take it off for a decrease.)

---

1  Express 12 kg as a percentage of 60 kg.
2  Find 35% of £120.
3  a  Increase £1000 by 20%.  b  Decrease £200 by 5%.

TEST

# Fractions, decimals & percentages

## ● Equivalents you should know

$\frac{1}{2} = 0.5 = 50\%$        $\frac{1}{10} = 0.1 = 10\%$        $\frac{1}{3} = 0.333... = 33\frac{1}{3}\%$

$\frac{1}{4} = 0.25 = 25\%$        $\frac{1}{100} = 0.01 = 1\%$        $\frac{2}{3} = 0.666... = 66\frac{2}{3}\%$

$\frac{3}{4} = 0.75 = 75\%$                $\frac{1}{8} = 0.125 = 12.5\%$

## ● Converting fractions to decimals

Divide the numerator by the denominator (use a written method or a calculator to do the division).

> ➤ **Example**
> $\frac{2}{5} = 2 \div 5 = 0.4$

## ● Converting percentages to fractions

Write the percentage as a fraction with denominator 100.

> ➤ $40\% = \frac{40}{100} = \frac{2}{5}$

Simplify if you can.

## ● Converting fractions to percentages

Write the fraction as an equivalent fraction with denominator 100.

Then write the numerator with a % sign.

> ➤ **Example**
> $\frac{1}{5} = \frac{20}{100} = 20\%$

## ● Converting percentages to decimals

This is pretty simple, just divide by 100. Remember to get rid of the % symbol.
(See page 8 for the easy way to divide by 100.)

> ➤ **Example**
> $15\% = 15 \div 100 = 0.15$

## ● Converting decimals to fractions

If there is one decimal place, write it over 10.

If there are two decimal places, write them over 100.

> ➤ **Examples**
> $0.8 = \frac{8}{10} = \frac{4}{5}$
> $0.12 = \frac{12}{100} = \frac{3}{25}$

Simplify fractions when possible.

---

**1** Convert to fractions: **a** 11% **b** 5% **c** 0.6 **d** 0.15

**2** Convert $\frac{7}{10}$ to **a** a decimal **b** a percentage.

**3** Convert 0.35 to a fraction.

TEST

# Ratio & proportion

## ● Proportion

'What proportion?' just means
'What fraction?',
'What percentage?' or
'What decimal?'

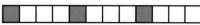
### ➤ Example

$\underline{1}$ in every $\underline{4}$ squares is shaded.

The proportion shaded is $\frac{1}{4}$ or
25% or 0.25.

## ● Ratio

In the example, 1 in every 4 squares is red.

So there is 1 red square for every 3 white squares.

The ratio of red to white squares is $1:3$

## ● Simplifying ratios

Ratios can be simplified like fractions.

Divide both sides by the same number.

If you can't divide any more you have the simplest form.

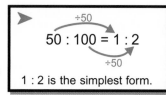

$$50:100 = 1:2$$
÷50 ... ÷50

1 : 2 is the simplest form.

## ● Solving problems

### ➤ Q & A

5 apples cost 90p.
How much would 8 apples cost?

**Answer**

| | |
|---|---|
| 5 apples cost: | 90p |
| 1 apple costs: | 90p ÷ 5 = 18p |
| 8 apples cost: | 18p × 8 = 144p or £1.44 |

### ➤ Method

❶ Divide by 5 to find the cost of 1.

❷ Multiply by 8 to find the cost of 8.

---

**1** What proportion of the squares are grey?
Give your answer as a fraction.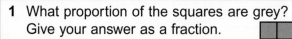

**2** What is the ratio of grey to white squares?
Give your answer in its simplest form.

**3** 3 kg of onions cost £1.92. How much would 2 kg cost?

TEST

*Speedy* Revision

# Calculations with brackets

## ● Order of operations

When faced with something like $5^2 - 2 \times (7 - 3)$ you have to work out each part in the correct order, else you'll get the wrong answer. Always do operations in this order:

| | |
|---|---|
| Brackets | $5^2 - 2 \times (7 - 3)$ |
| Squares | $= 5^2 - 2 \times 4$ |
| Divide and Multiply | $= 25 - 2 \times 4$ |
| Add and Subtract | $= 25 - 8$ |
| | $= 17$ |

BIDMAS

---

You can remember the order of operations with the word **BIDMAS**.
**B**rackets, then **I**ndices, **D**ivision, **M**ultiplication, **A**ddition, **S**ubtraction.
('Indices' is the fancy word for squares, cubes, etc.)

---

If there are several multiplications and divisions (or additions and subtractions) do them one at a time from <u>left to right</u>.

| For example: | Not: |
|---|---|
| $24 \div 6 \div 2$ | $24 \div 6 \div 2$ |
| $= 4 \div 2$ | $= 24 \div 3$ |
| $= 2$ ✔ | $= 8$ ✘ |

## ● Brackets on a calculator

Use the <u>bracket buttons</u>, **( )**, on your calculator <u>exactly where they appear</u> in a calculation. For $72 - (18 + 36)$ press:

**7** **2** **–** **(** **1** **8** **+** **3** **6** **)** **=** to get 18.

Look out for <u>sneaky brackets</u>:

$\frac{16 - 10}{2}$ is really $(16 - 10) \div 2$, so you have to <u>use brackets</u>.

Press: **(** **1** **6** **–** **1** **0** **)** **÷** **2** **=** ✔
Not: **1** **6** **–** **1** **0** **÷** **2** **=** ✘

---

Work these out on paper. Check your answers on a calculator.

**a** $3 \times 5 - 2 \times 4$  **b** $2.8 \times (15 - 2)$  **c** $56 \div 4 \div 2$  **d** $\frac{28}{(11 + 3)}$

TEST

# Using letters

In algebra, letters represent <u>unknown numbers</u> or numbers that can <u>change</u>.

Because the letters represent numbers, you can +, −, ×, ÷ them in exactly the same way:

$n - 1$ means <u>one less</u> than $n$

$n + 5$ means <u>five more</u> than $n$

$n + n$ means <u>two lots of $n$</u> or $2 \times n$

> ➤ **Example**
> Think of a number. I don't know what number you are thinking of, so I'll call it $n$.

You can use 'shorthand' when <u>multiplying</u>:

| For | $3 \times a$ | you write | $3a$ | (i.e. miss out the '×') |
|-----|-----|-----|-----|-----|
| For | $a \times b \times c$ | you write | $abc$ | |
| For | $a \times a \times a$ | you write | $a^3$ | (the raised 3 means that $a$ is multiplied by itself 3 times) |

## ● Terms and expressions

A <u>term</u> is some numbers and letters multiplied together.

$$4a + b + 3ab + 2$$

$a$ term     $b$ term     $ab$ term     number term

A collection of terms like this is called an <u>expression</u>.

## ● Collecting like terms

$4a$ and $3a$ are <u>like terms</u> because they have the <u>same letters</u>.

$2a$ and $5b$ are <u>not like terms</u> because they have <u>different letters</u>.

You can <u>simplify</u> expressions by <u>collecting like terms</u>.

$$4a \quad + \quad 3a \quad = \quad 7a$$

'<u>4</u> lots of $a$' and '<u>3</u> lots of $a$' makes '<u>7</u> lots of $a$'.

---

**1** I have $a$ apples. I eat one. How many are left?

**2** I write $n$ letters. Then I write 2 more. How many is that?

**3** Write these in 'shorthand': **a** $2 \times s \times t$   **b** $u \times u \times u \times u$

**4** Simplify these expressions by collecting like terms:

    **a** $t + t + t$   **b** $n + n + n + n$   **c** $y + 2y$   **d** $3x + 2 + x$

TEST

***Speedy* Revision**

# Brackets & algebraic fractions

## ● Multiplying out brackets

To get rid of brackets from an expression, you have to multiply everything inside the brackets by the term outside.
This is also called 'expanding brackets'.

> ### ➤ Examples

The 3 multiplies the $x$ and the 2.

$$3(x + 2) = 3 \times x + 3 \times 2 = 3x + 6$$

Outside   Inside

$$3(m - 4) = 3m - 12 \qquad x(y + z) = xy + xz \qquad a(4a + b) = 4a^2 + ab$$

If the term outside the brackets is negative, you have to change the sign of each term inside the brackets when you multiply out.

> ### ➤ Examples

$$-2(a + 3) = -2a - 6 \qquad\qquad -3(c - d) = -3c + 3d$$

A plus becomes a minus.          A minus becomes a plus.

## ● Adding simple algebraic fractions

Algebraic fractions are fractions with letters in such as $\frac{x}{5}$ or $\frac{2x + 3}{3}$.
They may look odd, but you just treat them as normal fractions.

### ➤ Q & A

Work out $\frac{x}{3} + \frac{4x}{3}$.

**Answer**

The denominators are the same, so it's just a case of adding the numerators: $\quad \frac{x}{3} + \frac{4x}{3} = \frac{x + 4x}{3} = \frac{5x}{3}$

---

**1** Multiply out these brackets:

   **a** $4(x + 2)$   **b** $m(n + 7)$   **c** $a(a + b)$   **d** $-4(d - 5)$

**2** Add these fractions:   **a** $\frac{2x}{5} + \frac{4x}{5}$   **b** $\frac{1}{d} + \frac{2}{d}$

TEST

# Equations

## ● Equations

An <u>equation</u> shows that two expressions are <u>equal</u>, e.g. $2x + 4 = 3x$.

## ● Solving equations

Solving equations is about finding the <u>value of the unknown</u> letter.
You can <u>add</u>, <u>subtract</u>, <u>multiply</u> or <u>divide</u> both sides by the same number, but you must do <u>exactly the same</u> thing <u>to both sides</u>.

### ➤ Q & A

Solve $7x - 4 = 10$ to find the value of $x$.

**Answer**

You need to end up with $x$ = something.

Get rid of the $- 4$ by adding 4 to both sides.

$$7x - 4 = 10$$

$$7x - 4 + 4 = 10 + 4 \qquad \text{[+4 to \underline{both} sides]}$$

$$7x = 14$$

Get rid of the × 7 by dividing both sides by 7 ($7x$ means $x × 7$).

$$7x ÷ 7 = 14 ÷ 7 \qquad \text{[÷ \underline{both} sides by 7]}$$

$$\underline{x = 2}$$

## ● Two important examples

There are two further types of equations they could throw at you:

**❶** <u>The equation contains brackets</u>, e.g. $2(x + 5) = 18$
The first thing to do is to <u>multiply out the brackets</u> (see previous page).
Here, the equation becomes $2x + 10 = 18$.
You then solve it as normal (like above **Q & A**, but $-10$ then $÷2$).

**❷** <u>The unknown letter appears on both sides</u>, e.g. $5x = 2x + 6$
You need to get the <u>letters</u> on <u>one side</u> and <u>numbers</u> on the <u>other</u>.
In this case, subtract $2x$ from both sides to get $3x = 6$.
You then solve it as normal (try dividing both sides by 3 ...)

---

**1** Solve these equations: **a** $2x + 5 = 11$ **b** $3x - 8 = 16$
**2** Finish solving the 'Two important examples', then solve:
   **a** $4(2x + 3) = 28$ **b** $10x = 3x + 14$

TEST

# Formulae & substitution

## ● Formulae

A <u>formula</u> is basically a rule that <u>turns one number into another</u>.

> ### ➤ Example

Jo has a machine that makes chocolate biscuits.
One packet of biscuit mix makes four biscuits.

You can write this as a formula in words:

<u>Number of biscuits = 4 × the number of packets of biscuit mix</u>

You can also write this with algebra as <u>$B = 4P$</u>,
where <u>$B$</u> represents <u>the number of biscuits</u> and <u>$P$</u> represents
<u>the number of packets of biscuit mix</u>.

## ● Substituting numbers into formulae & expressions

You can <u>substitute</u> a number into an <u>expression</u> to find its value.

To substitute $y = 3$ into $2y + 5$, just write '3' in place of '$y$' then work out the answer.

> When $y = 3$:    $2y + 5$
>
> $= 2 \times 3 + 5$
>
> $= 6 + 5$
>
> $= 11$

The trickiest substitution they could give you is one involving squares or cubes:

## ➤ Q & A

Given the formula $y = 4x^3$, find the value of $y$ when $x = 2$.

**Answer**

Write out the formula again with 2 in the place of $x$:

$y = 4 \times 2^3$ ← $2^3$ means 2 times by itself 3 times

$= 4 \times 2 \times 2 \times 2$

$= \underline{32}$ ← Double 4, then double again, then double again!

---

1  A plumber charges £25 per hour. Write a formula, in algebra, for the charge ($C$) in terms of number of hours worked ($h$).
2  Use your formula from **Q1** to work out the charge for 8 hours.
3  Work out the value of $a$ when $b = 3$ in these formulae:
   **a** $a = 3b + 2$   **b** $a = 2b^2 + 1$

TEST

# Sequences & number patterns (1)

A <u>sequence</u> is a list of numbers that <u>follows</u> <u>a pattern</u> or rule.

> Each number in a sequence is called a <u>term</u>.
>
> 2, 4, 6, 8, ...
>
> 3rd term

## ● **Adding or subtracting patterns**

This is where a number is added or subtracted to get the next term in the sequence.

## ● **Multiplying or dividing patterns**

Here you multiply or divide to get the next term.

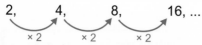

## ● **Sequence diagrams**

You can also get a sequence of <u>diagrams</u>. The trick is to convert the diagrams into a sequence of <u>numbers</u>.

> ➤ **Example**
> Here is a sequence of diagrams:
>
> To find the number of squares in the next diagram you need to count the number of squares in each diagram and write this as a sequence of numbers.
>
>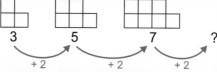
>
> The next diagram will have 7 + 2 = <u>9 squares</u>.
>
>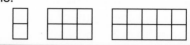

---

1. What is the next term in each of these sequences?
   **a** 5, 8, 11, 14, ...  **b** 3, 6, 12, 24, ...  **c** 21, 17, 13, 9, ...
2. Here is a sequence of diagrams. How many squares are in the next diagram?

TEST

*Speedy* Revision

# Sequences & number patterns (2)

## ● *n*th term

The *n*th term is an expression used to find <u>any</u> term in a sequence.

> ### ➤ Example
>
> If someone tells you that the <u>*n*th</u> term of a sequence is $\underline{3n + 4}$, then you can quickly work out any term in the sequence.
>
> The <u>1st</u> term is $3 \times \underline{1} + 4 = 7$, and the <u>100th</u> term is $3 \times \underline{100} + 4 = 304$.
>
> Just substitute the term number in place of *n*.

## ● Finding the *n*th term

You might be asked to find the *n*th term of an adding or subtracting pattern/sequence.

You need to learn this method:

### ➤ Q & A

Find the *n*th term of this sequence:  6, 10, 14, 18, ...

**Answer**

❶ The difference between terms is <u>4</u>.

❷ Write out the <u>4</u> times-table: 4, 8, 12, 16, ...

### ➤ Foolproof method for finding the *n*th term

❶ Find the <u>difference</u> between the terms.

❷ Write out the <u>times-table</u> for the difference found in ❶.

❸ <u>Compare</u> the times-table to the original sequence.

❸ The original sequence is always <u>2 more</u> than the 4 times-table.

$$4 + 2, 8 + 2, 12 + 2, 16 + 2, ... \quad ⅢⅢ➡ \quad 6, 10, 14, 18, ...$$

This means that the *n*th term is <u>$4n + 2$</u>.

The 4*n* gives the 4 times-table for *n* = 1, 2, 3, and so on. ←

→ The +2 is needed because the sequence is 2 more than the 4 times-table.

---

**1** The *n*th term of a sequence is $2n + 5$.
   Find these terms in the sequence:
   **a** 1st term   **b** 50th term   **c** 100th term

**2** Work out the *n*th term in these sequences:
   **a** 7, 10, 13, 16, 19, ...
   **b** 1, 5, 9, 13, 17, ...

**TEST**

# Functions & mappings

## ● Functions

A <u>function</u> (also called a <u>mapping</u>) changes an <u>input to an output</u>.

❶ Functions can be written in words, e.g.
'<u>multiply the input by 3 to get the output</u>'.

❷ Functions can be demonstrated by <u>function machines</u>:

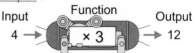

Input
4 →

Function

× 3

Output
→ 12

❸ Functions can be illustrated by <u>mapping diagrams</u>:

1 ⟶ 3
2 ⟶ 6
3 ⟶ 9

❹ Functions can be described using <u>algebra</u> (<u>letters</u>):

$x \longrightarrow 3x$

Think of this as '$x$ becomes 3 times $x$'.

### ▶ Q & A

Input ⟶ × 2 ▸ + 4 ⟶ Output

a   What is the output for the function machine when the input is 6?
b   What is the input for the function machine when the output is 10?
c   Write the function machine as a function using algebra.

**Answer**

a   The machine has two steps. First '× 2', then '+ 4'.
    6 × 2 = 12, 12 + 4 = <u>16</u>
b   Start at the right (the output) and go backwards to the left.
    So starting with 10 you need to '− 4' then '÷ 2' (division is the
    opposite of multiplication, subtraction is the opposite of addition).
    10 − 4 = 6, 6 ÷ 2 = <u>3</u>
c   Here you need to put a letter into the machine.
    Putting $x$ in gives $2x$ after the first step and then $2x + 4$ after the
    second step, so the function is $x \to \underline{2x + 4}$.

---

**1**  a  For this function machine, what
          is the output when the input is 4?

→ × 5 + 2 →

   b  What is the input when the output is 12?
   c  Write the function machine as a function using algebra.
**2**  Draw the function in **Q1** as a mapping diagram with inputs
       1, 2, 3 and 4.

TEST

# Coordinates

## ● **Coordinates**

Coordinates are pairs of numbers that give the <u>positions of points</u> on a graph.

The *y*-axis is vertical.

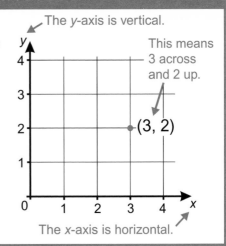

This means 3 across and 2 up.

$$(x, y)$$

The <u>first number</u> of the pair is called the <u>*x*-coordinate</u>; the <u>second number</u> is called the <u>*y*-coordinate</u>. (Notice they are in alphabetical order, i.e. *x* comes before *y*.)

The *x*-axis is horizontal.

## ● **Negative coordinates**

To plot points that have negative coordinates you need to extend the axes back past zero. This splits the graph into <u>4 different sections</u>.

A is at (2, 1)
B is at (−4, 1)
C is at (−2, −4)
D is at (3, −1)

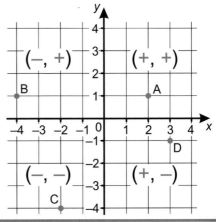

Remember: the first coordinate corresponds to the horizontal axis.

Write down the coordinates of the points on the graph on the right.

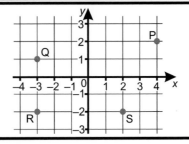

**TEST**

# Straight-line graphs (1)

## ● Plotting and drawing straight-line graphs

The secret to drawing graphs is to first construct a <u>table of values</u>.

### ➤ Q & A

Complete this table of values for the equation $y = 2x + 2$ and then draw its graph.

| x | −2 | −1 | 0 | 1 | 2 |
|---|---|---|---|---|---|
| y = 2x + 2 | | 0 | | 4 | |

**Answer**

The missing values are when $x = -2$, $x = 0$ and $x = 2$.
Putting these values into the equation gives:

when $x = -2$:  $y = 2x + 2 = 2 \times (-2) + 2 = -4 + 2 = \underline{-2}$
when $x = 0$:  $y = 2x + 2 = 2 \times 0 + 2 = 0 + 2 = \underline{2}$
when $x = 2$:  $y = 2x + 2 = 2 \times 2 + 2 = 4 + 2 = \underline{6}$

So the completed table is:

| x | −2 | −1 | 0 | 1 | 2 |
|---|---|---|---|---|---|
| y = 2x + 2 | −2 | 0 | 2 | 4 | 6 |

Next plot the points one at a time on graph paper:

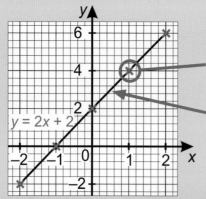

This pair of values gives the point (1, 4).

(1, 4) is plotted here.

Finally, use a <u>ruler</u> to draw a straight line through the points.

---

**a** Copy and complete the table of values for the equation: $y = 3x + 2$.

| x | −2 | −1 | 0 | 1 | 2 |
|---|---|---|---|---|---|
| y = 3x + 2 | −4 | | | 5 | |

**b** Draw the graph of $y = 3x + 2$ on graph paper.
(The x-axis should go from −2 to 2 and the y-axis should go from −4 to 8.)

**TEST**

**Speedy** Revision

# Straight-line graphs (2)

## ● Finding the gradient of a straight line

> ### Method
> ❶ Pick two points on the line.
> ❷ Draw a triangle through the points.
> ❸ Work out the height of the triangle and the width of the triangle.
> ❹ Use this formula to work out the gradient of the line:
>
> $$\text{Gradient} = \frac{\text{height}}{\text{width}}$$

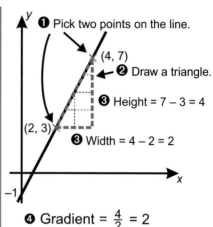

❶ Pick two points on the line.

(4, 7)

❷ Draw a triangle.

❸ Height = 7 − 3 = 4

(2, 3)

❸ Width = 4 − 2 = 2

❹ Gradient = $\frac{4}{2}$ = 2

## ● Positive or negative gradient?

If the graph <u>slopes upwards</u> ( ╱ ) the gradient will be <u>positive</u>.

If the graph <u>slopes downwards</u> ( ╲ ) the gradient will be <u>negative</u>.

## ● The general equation of a line is $y = mx + c$

All equations of straight lines can be written in the form <u>$y = mx + c$</u>.

m is the <u>gradient</u>. The greater the value of m the steeper the graph.

c is the <u>y-intercept</u>. This tells you the line cuts the <u>y-axis at (0, c)</u>.

> The line above has gradient <u>2</u> and cuts the y-axis at $y = \underline{-1}$.
> So the equation of the line is <u>$y = 2x - 1$</u>.

## ● Vertical and horizontal lines

<u>$x = a$</u> is the equation of a <u>vertical line</u> that cuts the x-axis at <u>(a, 0)</u>.

<u>$y = b$</u> is the equation of a <u>horizontal line</u> that cuts the y-axis at <u>(0, b)</u>.

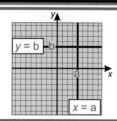

Write down the equation of the line that has gradient 5 and goes through the point (0, 4).

TEST

# Real-life graphs

## ● Real-life straight-line graphs

The trick, again, is to first construct a <u>table of values</u>.

➤ Christina is taking part in a sponsored run. For every mile she runs she will raise £5 for her charity.

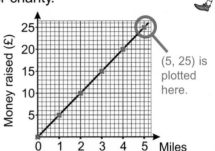

| Miles run | Money raised |
|-----------|--------------|
| 0 | £0 |
| 1 | £5 |
| 2 | £10 |
| 3 | £15 |
| 4 | £20 |
| 5 | £25 |

She raises £5 for 1 mile so she'll raise £5 × 5 = £25 for 5 miles.

(5, 25) is plotted here.

## ● Distance–time graphs

In a <u>distance–time graph</u> the <u>gradient</u> gives the <u>velocity</u> (speed).

### ➤ Q & A

The graph shows Suki's walk to and from a local shop. Describe her journey in words.

**Answer**

❶ She starts <u>walking slowly</u>.
❷ She <u>stops</u> for a short while, perhaps because she bumps into a friend.
❸ She starts <u>walking more quickly</u>.
❹ She <u>stops</u> in the shop for a while.
❺ She <u>walks home without stopping</u>.

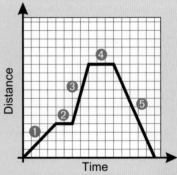

1 Describe the train journey shown in the graph.

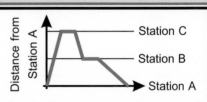

Station C
Station B
Station A

Distance from Station A

**TEST**

2 Calculate the gradient of the line in the sponsored run graph.

# Units of measurement

## ● Metric units

Commonly used metric units of length are
millimetre (mm), centimetre (cm), metre (m),
kilometre (km); masses are gram (g), kilogram
(kg); capacities are millilitre (ml), litre (l).

**Length**
10 mm = 1 cm
100 cm = 1 m
1000 m = 1 km
**Mass**
1000 g = 1 kg
**Capacity**
1000 ml = 1 litre

## ● Converting between metric units

Metric units are based on the decimal system
and so it is easy to convert between them.

- To change from small units to large units divide.
- To change from large units to small units multiply.

### ➤ Examples
300 cm = 3 m (÷ 100)
7 litres = 7000 ml (× 1000)
5000 g = 5 kg (÷ 1000)
30 cm = 300 mm (× 10)

Divide because this is going from small to
large units. The 100 comes from the fact
that 100 cm = 1 m.

Multiply because this is going from large
to small units. The 10 comes from the fact
that 10 mm = 1 cm.

## ● Imperial units

**Length**
12 inches = 1 foot
3 feet = 1 yard
**Mass**
16 ounces = 1 pound
**Capacity**
8 pints = 1 gallon

Imperial units are getting
a bit old fashioned.

## ● Converting between metric and imperial units

**Length**
1 foot is roughly 30 cm
1 mile is roughly 1.6 km
**Mass**
1 pound is roughly 450 g
1 ounce is roughly 30 g
**Capacity**
1 pint is roughly 0.5 litre
1 gallon is roughly 4.5 litres

1  Convert these to centimetres: **a** 2 m  **b** 60 mm
2  How many grams in: **a** an ounce  **b** a pound?

TEST

# Appropriate units & reading scales

## ● Choosing the appropriate units of measurement

You need to use the correct units when measuring something.

| Millimetres (mm) | Centimetres (cm) | Metres (m) | Kilometres (km) |
|---|---|---|---|
|  |  |  |  |
| Thickness of a book | Height of a TV | Height of a tall building | Distance to the moon |
| **Millilitres (ml)** | **Litres (l)** | **Grams (g)** | **Kilograms (kg)** |
|  |  |  |  |
| Liquid in a test tube | Water in a bath | Mass of a red-hot chilli | Mass of a dishwasher |

## ● Reading scales

You should always work out how much each division is worth.

> ## ➤ Examples

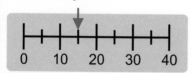

There are 2 spaces between 10 and 20.
So each space is worth 5.
The reading shows <u>15</u>.

There are 5 spaces between 20 and 30.
So each space is worth 2.
The reading shows <u>26</u>.

---

1  What unit would you use to measure the: **a** height of a giraffe
   **b** amount of water in a pond  **c** weight of a mouse?

2  Read these scales:

   **a**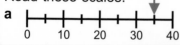

   **b**

Speedy Revision

# Estimating & measuring angles

## ● An angle is a measure of turn

$\frac{1}{4}$ turn = <u>90°</u>      $\frac{1}{2}$ turn = <u>180°</u>      $\frac{3}{4}$ turn = <u>270°</u>      Full turn = <u>360°</u>

### ▶ Q & A

Estimate the size of this angle:

**Answer**

You need to compare the angle to 90°, 180°, 270° and 360°.

The angle is more than 180° but less than 270°. A good estimate would be <u>210°</u>.

## ● Measuring angles with a protractor

Before measuring you must <u>estimate</u> the size of the angle.

This angle is acute. It looks about 45° (half a right angle).

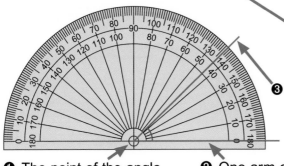

❸ Read the angle from the correct scale. The estimate was 45° so it must be <u>44°</u> (not 136°).

❶ The point of the angle should be at the cross.

❷ One arm of the angle should be along the 0° line.

---

**1** Estimate the size of these angles.    **a**    **b**

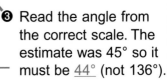

**2** Measure the angles in **Q1** with a protractor.

TEST

# Angles & parallel lines

## ● Angle facts

An <u>acute angle</u> is less than 90°.

A <u>right angle</u> is 90°.

An <u>obtuse angle</u> is between 90° and 180°.

A <u>reflex angle</u> is more than 180°.

---

**Angles on a straight line add up to 180°.**

$$a + b = 180°$$

---

**Angles at a point add up to 360°.**

$$c + d + e + f = 360°$$

---

**Vertically opposite angles are equal.**

$$p = r \text{ and } q = s$$

## ● Parallel lines

**Alternate angles are equal.**

$$u = v$$

(The angles are in a Z-shape.)

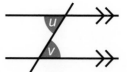

---

**Corresponding angles are equal.**

$$w = x$$

(The angles are in an F-shape.)

---

Work out the size of the lettered angles.

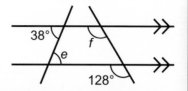

**TEST**

40

# Polygons

- ● **The angles in a triangle add up to 180°**

  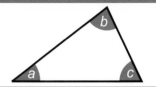

  $$a + b + c = 180°$$

- ● **The angles in a quadrilateral add up to 360°**

  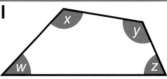

  $$w + x + y + z = 360°$$

- ● **Interior and exterior angles**

  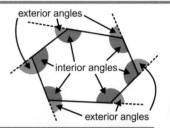

  The angles <u>inside</u> a polygon are called <u>interior angles</u>.

  <u>Exterior angles</u> are found on the <u>outside</u> when the <u>sides are extended</u>.

  <u>Learn</u> these two formulae:

  > ❶ Sum of exterior angles = 360°
  >
  > ❷ Sum of interior angles = (number of sides − 2) × 180°

- ● **Regular polygons**

  The <u>sides and angles</u> of a <u>regular polygon</u> are all the <u>same size</u>.

➤ **Q & A**

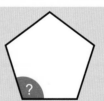

What is the size of an interior angle in a regular pentagon?

**Answer**

Using formula ❷ above we get:

Sum of interior angles of a regular pentagon = (5 − 2) × 180° = 540°

There are 5 equal interior angles, so size of one = 540° ÷ 5 = <u>108°</u>

---

1 Two interior angles of a triangle are 57° and 74°. What size is the other angle?

2 What size are the interior and exterior angles of
   **a** a square   **b** a regular hexagon?

**TEST**

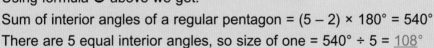

# Symmetry & properties of shapes (1)

## ● Reflection symmetry

If a shape can be folded so that one half fits exactly on the other, it is said to have reflection symmetry (also known as line symmetry).

Fold line (also called mirror line)

Some shapes have more than one line of symmetry; some don't have any:

| Square<br>4 lines of symmetry | Equilateral triangle<br>3 lines of symmetry | No lines of symmetry |

## ● Rotation symmetry

A shape has rotation symmetry if it looks exactly the same when turned. The order of rotation symmetry is the number of times a shape fits exactly over itself during a full-turn about its centre.

### ➤ Q & A

What is the order of rotation symmetry of these shapes?

Order 4        Order 3        Order 1

**Note:** Order of rotation symmetry 1 means no rotation symmetry.

## ● Plane symmetry

This is basically reflection symmetry in 3-D shapes.
A plane of symmetry cuts a solid shape in half so that one half is the mirror image of the other.

### ➤ Q & A

Draw a cube and an isosceles triangular prism. Indicate one plane of symmetry in each.

Answer

Both of these shapes have more than one plane of symmetry. See TEST Q2.

*Speedy* Revision

# Symmetry & properties of shapes (2)

## ● **Four types of triangle**

### Right-angled
One 90° angle

### Isosceles
2 equal sides
2 equal angles
1 line of symmetry

### Equilateral
3 equal sides
3 equal angles
3 lines of symmetry
Rotation symmetry of order 3

### Scalene
All sides and angles
are different

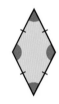

## ● **Quadrilaterals (shapes with 4 sides)**

### Square
4 lines of symmetry
Rotation symmetry
of order 4
All angles are 90°
All sides equal
2 pairs of parallel sides

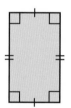

### Rhombus
2 lines of symmetry
Rotation symmetry
of order 2
All sides equal
Opposite angles equal
2 pairs of parallel sides

### Rectangle
2 lines of symmetry
Rotation symmetry
of order 2
All angles are 90°
Opposite sides equal
2 pairs of parallel sides

### Kite
1 line of symmetry
No rotation symmetry
2 pairs of adjacent sides
equal
1 pair of opposite angles equal

### Trapezium
No lines of symmetry
(unless isosceles)
No rotation symmetry
One pair of parallel sides

### Parallelogram
No lines of symmetry
Rotation symmetry
of order 2
Opposite sides
equal and parallel
Opposite angles equal

Parallel lines never meet.
Perpendicular lines cross at right angles.

**1** For each shape write down the: **i** number of lines of symmetry
**ii** order of rotation symmetry.

   **a**      **b**      **c**

**2** Draw a different plane of symmetry on the cube and
isosceles triangular prism on the previous page.

**TEST**

# Reflection

## ● Reflecting a shape in a mirror line

When you reflect a shape in a mirror line its size and shape are <u>not</u> changed. The original shape is called the <u>object</u> and its reflection is called the <u>image</u>.

### ➤ Q & A

Reflect the shape in the mirror line.

**Answer**

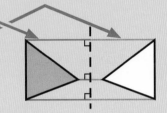

❶ Draw a line from each corner <u>at right angles</u> to the mirror line.
❷ Extend the lines exactly the same distance on the other side of the mirror line.
❸ Join up the ends of the lines to show the image.

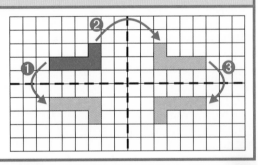

## ● Two mirror lines

You can make a symmetrical pattern by reflecting in two mirror lines.

Keep reflecting until the pattern is complete.

---

Copy and then reflect these shapes in the mirror lines:

**a**

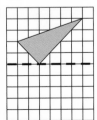

**b**

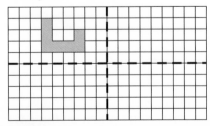

TEST

*Speedy* Revision

# Rotation

## ● Turning shapes

A rotation turns a shape through an angle about some fixed point.

A rotation can be in a <u>clockwise</u> or <u>anticlockwise</u> direction.

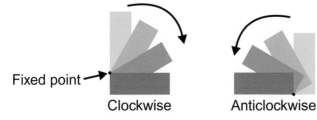

Fixed point →

Clockwise          Anticlockwise

### ➤ Q & A

Rotate the shape 90° <u>clockwise</u> about the corner marked with a dot.

**Answer**

❶ Draw around the shape on tracing paper.

❷ Pin the tracing paper down with your pencil at the dot.

❸ Rotate the tracing paper 90° clockwise.

❹ Draw over the traced shape (press down quite hard) so that you can see where to draw the rotated shape.

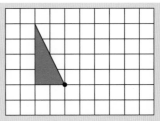

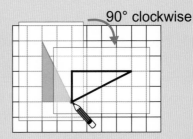

90° clockwise

Rotate these shapes 90° <u>anticlockwise</u> about the dots:

a

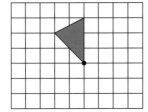

b

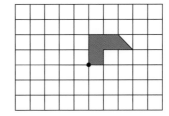

TEST

# Translation

## ● Sliding shapes

A translation is where you slide a shape along <u>without</u> rotating or reflecting it.

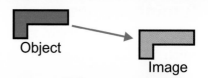

Object

Image

A translation moves a shape:
① a specific distance <u>left or right</u>
② and then a specific distance <u>up or down</u>.

### ➤ Q & A

Translate the triangle 5 squares to the right and 3 squares up.

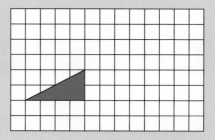

**Answer**

❶ Put your pencil on a corner of the shape.
❷ Move your pencil 5 squares right and 3 squares up.
❸ Draw the shape in the new position.

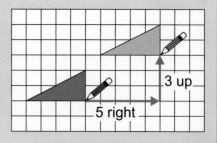

3 up

5 right

**1** Translate the shape 4 units to the right and 2 units up.

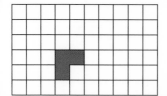

**2** Translate the shape 5 units to the left and 2 units down.

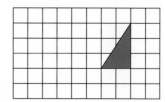

*Speedy* Revision

# Enlargement

## ● Centres of enlargements & scale factors

An <u>enlargement</u> changes the <u>size</u> of an object, but not its shape.
To describe an enlargement you give its <u>centre</u> and <u>scale factor</u>.

### ➤ Example

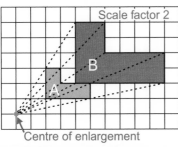

Scale factor 2

Centre of enlargement

The sides of shape B are all <u>twice as long</u> as the sides of shape A because the <u>scale factor</u> of the enlargement is <u>2</u>.

The corners of shape B are <u>twice as far from the centre of enlargement</u>, on lines drawn through the corners of shape A.

### ➤ Q & A

Shape D is an enlargement of shape C.
What is the scale factor of the enlargement?

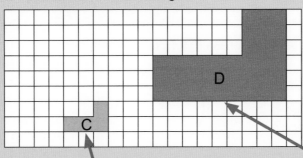

**Answer**

The base of shape C is <u>3</u> squares long; the base of shape D is <u>9</u> squares long. So the scale factor is 9 ÷ 3 = <u>3</u>.

---

1  Enlarge the triangle on the right by scale factor 2 and centre at the dot.

2  Copy the diagram in the Q & A above. Mark on the centre of enlargement.
(Draw lines through corresponding corners and see where they meet.)

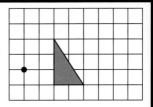

TEST

# Perimeter & circumference

## ● Perimeter

Perimeter is the distance around the outside edge of a 2-D shape. It is measured in mm, cm, m or km.

### ➤ Q & A

What is the perimeter of this shape?

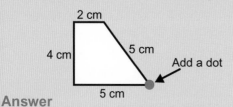

2 cm
4 cm
5 cm
Add a dot
5 cm

**Answer**

Start at the dot and add the sides up clockwise: 5 + 4 + 2 + 5 = 16 cm

### ➤ Method
❶ Mark a corner with a dot.
❷ Start at the dot, add the sides as you go around the shape. Stop when you get back to the dot.
❸ Essential: Show your working.

## ● Circumference of a circle

The circumference is the perimeter of a circle.

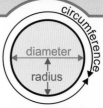

circumference
diameter
radius

Circumference = π × diameter ($C = \pi d$)

π ≈ 3.14 or 3.142 or press **π** (π is a Greek letter, pronounced 'pie'.)

### ➤ Q & A

This circle has a radius of 5 cm. What is its circumference?

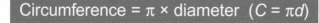

5 cm

**Answer**

The radius is 5 cm, so the diameter = 5 cm × 2 = 10 cm.

Circumference = π × diameter = 3.14 × 10 = 31.4 cm

### ➤ Method
❶ Find the diameter (the diameter is twice the radius).
❷ Use the formula: $C = \pi d$

---

**1** Work out the perimeters of these shapes:

a

4 cm
10 cm

b

2 cm
2 cm
4 cm
10 cm

TEST

**2** What is the circumference of a circle with radius 8 cm?

48

# Area of 2-D shapes (1)

## ● Area

The <u>area</u> of a 2-D shape is the <u>amount of space</u> it covers.
It is measured in <u>mm²</u>, <u>cm²</u>, <u>m²</u> or <u>km²</u>.◄——— Notice the 'squared' bit.

If the shape is drawn on a square grid you can work out the area by <u>counting squares</u>. If not you'll have to use a <u>formula</u>:

## ● Area of a triangle

Area = $\frac{1}{2}$ × base × height

$A = \frac{1}{2} \times b \times h$

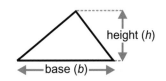

## ● Area of a rectangle

Area = length × width

$A = l \times w$

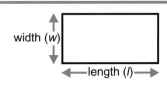

## ● Area of a parallelogram

Area = base × perpendicular height

$A = b \times h$

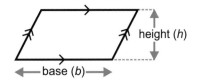

## ● Area of a trapezium

Area = $\frac{1}{2}$ × sum of parallel sides × height between them

$A = \frac{1}{2} \times (a + b) \times h$

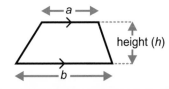

<u>Essential:</u> for <u>triangles</u>, <u>parallelograms</u>
and <u>trapeziums</u> make sure that you use
the <u>height</u> that's at <u>right angles to the base</u>.

## ➤ Example

Use the perpendicular height...

The area of this parallelogram
= base × perpendicular height
= 10 × 7 = <u>70 m²</u>.

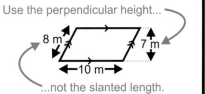

...not the slanted length.

# Area of 2-D shapes (2)

## ● Area of a circle

Area = π × radius squared

$$A = \pi r^2$$

Use the **π** button
(or π ≈ 3.14 or 3.142).

### ➤ Q & A

A circular window has a diameter of 18 m.
Find the area of the window.

**Answer**

The <u>diameter</u> is 18 m, so the

<u>radius</u> = 18 m ÷ 2 = 9 m.

Area = π × $r^2$

= 3.14 × 9² = 3.14 × 81 = <u>254.34 m²</u> ◄ Remember the squared units.

### ➤ Method

❶ Find the radius
(<u>the radius is half
the diameter</u>).

❷ Use the formula:
$A = \pi r^2$

---

<u>Memorise</u> the formulae on this page and the previous one
(get someone to test you), then work out the areas of these
shapes (remember your units):

**a**

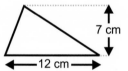

7 cm

12 cm

**b**

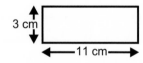

3 cm

11 cm

**c**

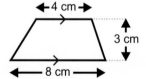

4 cm

3 cm

8 cm

**d**

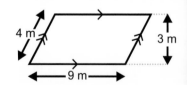

4 m

3 m

9 m

**e**

8 cm

**f**

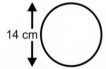

14 cm

TEST

# Nets & 3-D shapes; plans & elevations

## ● Nets

A <u>net</u> is a 3-D shape folded out <u>flat</u>.
Below are some 3-D shapes, with
their nets, that you need to know.

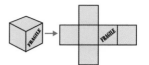

### Cube

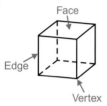

Face

Edge

Vertex

There are 11 different nets for a cube.
Here are two, can you draw the others? (See p70)

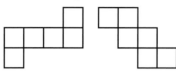

### Cuboid

### Square-based pyramid

### Triangular prism

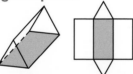

### Regular tetrahedron

## ● Plans & elevations

A <u>plan</u> of a 3-D shape is what you see if you look down from <u>above</u>.
An <u>elevation</u> is what you see if you look from the <u>front or side</u>.

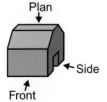

Plan

Side

Front

Plan    Front    Side

---

**1** How many faces, edges and vertices do these have?
   **a** cuboid   **b** triangular prism
**2** Draw plan, front and side elevations for a triangular prism.

TEST

# Surface area

Before you try this page make sure you understand everything on the previous page.

## ● Surface area

The <u>surface area</u> of a 3-D shape is the <u>total area</u> of all its <u>faces</u>. This is the same as the <u>area of its net</u>.

### ➤ Q & A

Work out the surface area of this cuboid.

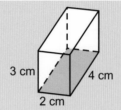

3 cm   4 cm
2 cm

**Answer**

First sketch the net of the cuboid.

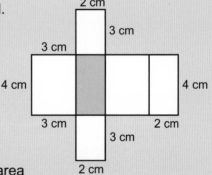

2 cm
3 cm
3 cm
4 cm   4 cm
3 cm   2 cm
3 cm
2 cm

The task now is to work out the area of each of the six rectangles (faces).

Two have an area of 2 cm × 3 cm = 6 cm²
two have an area of 2 cm × 4 cm = 8 cm²
and two have an area of 3 cm × 4 cm = 12 cm².

So the total surface area is 6 + 6 + 8 + 8 + 12 + 12 = <u>52 cm²</u>.

---

Work out the surface area of each of these shapes:

**a**

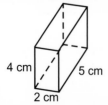

4 cm   5 cm
2 cm

**b**

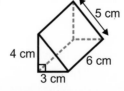

5 cm
4 cm   6 cm
3 cm

(You'll need to work out the area of the triangular ends: see page 49 for the formula.)

**TEST**

**Speedy Revision**

# Volume

## ● Volume

The <u>volume</u> of a 3-D solid is the <u>amount of space</u> it takes up.
It is measured in <u>mm³</u>, <u>cm³</u>, <u>m³</u> or <u>km³</u>. ← Notice the 'cubed' bit.

If the shape is made from cubes you can find the volume by
<u>counting the cubes</u>. If not you'll have to use a <u>formula</u>:

## ● Volume of a cuboid

Volume = length × width × height

$V = l × w × h$

(This formula also works for
a cube, i.e. $V = l × l × l = l^3$.)

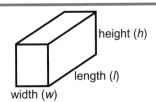

height (h)

length (l)

width (w)

## ● Volume of a prism

Volume = area of cross-section × length

$V = A × l$

(A prism is a shape with the same
cross-section all along its length.)

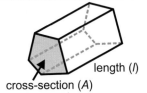

length (l)

cross-section (A)

## ➤ Q & A

Work out the volume of
this triangular prism:

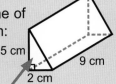

5 cm

9 cm

2 cm

**Answer**

The <u>area</u> of the <u>cross-section</u>
(triangular end) is
$\frac{1}{2} × 2 × 5 = 5$ cm².

The <u>length</u> is 9 cm.
So <u>volume</u> = $A × l = 5 × 9 =$ <u>45 cm³</u>.

## ➤ Method

❶ Work out the <u>area</u>
of the <u>cross-section</u>.

❷ Write down the <u>length</u>
of the prism.

❸ Use the formula
<u>$V = A × l$</u>
to work out the volume.

❹ Remember your <u>units</u>
(usually cm³ or m³).

---

Work out the volumes of these shapes:

**a**

4 cm

5 cm

2 cm

**b**

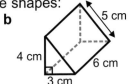

5 cm

4 cm

6 cm

3 cm

(You'll need to
work out the area
of the triangular
ends: see page 49
for the formula.)

TEST

# Bearings & scale drawings

## ● Bearings

❶ A bearing is <u>an angle</u> that gives a <u>direction</u>.

❷ Bearings are measured <u>clockwise</u> from the <u>North line</u>.

❸ All bearings are given as <u>3 figures</u>.

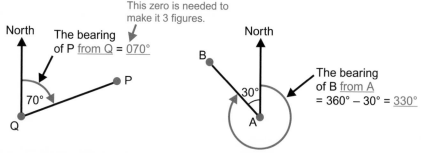

This zero is needed to make it 3 figures.

North

The bearing of P <u>from Q</u> = <u>070°</u>

70°

Q

● P

North

B

30°

A

The bearing of B <u>from A</u> = 360° − 30° = <u>330°</u>

Look out for the word <u>from</u>; it tells you where to draw the North line and measure <u>from</u>.

## ● Scale drawings & maps

Scale drawings usually have a scale something like '<u>1 cm = 5 m</u>'. This means that a length of <u>1 cm on the drawing</u> represents a distance of <u>5 m in real life</u>. A scale can also be given as a <u>ratio</u>, e.g. 1 cm = 5 m can be written as <u>1 : 500</u>.

### ➤ Example

The map shows the positions of three towns.

The distance between Berlham and Carwick is <u>3 cm</u> on the map.

The scale is <u>1 cm = 20 km</u>, so this means that the distance in real life is <u>20 km × 3 = 60 km</u>.

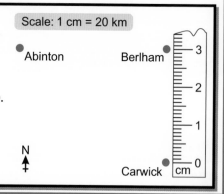

Scale: 1 cm = 20 km

● Abinton    Berlham ●

N

Carwick ●

---

**1** In the example above, what is the bearing of:
  **a** Berlham from Abinton   **b** Abinton from Berlham?
**2** What is the distance in real life between Abinton and Carwick?

TEST

# Constructions & loci (1)

## ● How to construct an equilateral triangle

❶

❷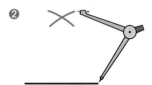

❸ You've also constructed an angle of 60°.

Draw a line of the length you want the sides to be, e.g. 5 cm.

Set your compasses to 5 cm. Draw two crossing arcs from the ends of the line.

Join the point where the arcs crossed to the ends of the line.

## ● Perpendicular bisector of a line

Perpendicular means 'at right angles'. Bisect means 'cut in half'.

This is similar to constructing an equilateral triangle.

You just have to draw two more crossing arcs on the other side of the line.

Set your compasses to more than half the length of the line.

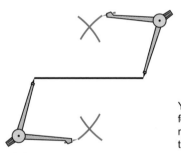

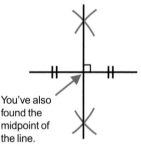

You've also found the midpoint of the line.

## ● Perpendicular from a point to a line

❶ Draw two arcs on the line, centred on the point. Keep your compasses set at the same distance.

❷ Draw two crossing arcs on the other side of the line, with the compasses centred on the arcs on the line.

Line

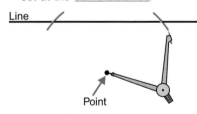

Point

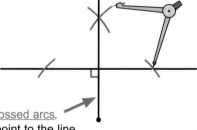

❸ Draw a line from the point to the crossed arcs. This is the perpendicular from the point to the line.

---

1 Construct an equilateral triangle of side 6 cm.
2 Draw a line 8 cm long. Construct its perpendicular bisector.
3 Construct the perpendicular from a point to a line.

TEST

# Constructions & loci (2)

## ● **Perpendicular from a point on a line**

**①**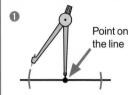
Point on the line

**②**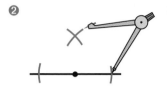

**③**

Draw arcs on the line either side of the point. Use the same radius.

Increase the radius. Draw two crossing arcs centred on the arcs on the line.

Join the original point to where the arcs crossed. This is the perpendicular.

## ● **Bisector of an angle**

**①**

**②**

**③**
The line cuts the angle in half.

Draw two arcs on the arms of the angle, centred on the vertex.

Draw two crossing arcs inside the angle, centred on the arcs on the arms.

Join the vertex to the point where the arcs crossed.

## ● **Loci**

A locus is a set of points (often lines) that satisfy a given rule. Here are four loci that you should know (loci are in colour):

**①**

**②**

**③**

**④**

A fixed distance from a point is a circle.

A fixed distance from a straight line is two parallel straight lines.

Equidistant from two points is the perpendicular bisector of the line joining the two points.

Equidistant from two straight lines is the bisectors of the angles between the lines.

Types ① & ② are often combined:
Fixed distance from a line segment

1 Construct a perpendicular 5 cm from the end of a 14 cm line.
2 Draw a 68° angle with a protractor. Bisect it with compasses.
3 Construct the locus of points 4 cm from a line 6 cm long.

TEST

56

*Speedy* Revision

# Collecting data & two-way tables

## ● Collecting data

Two ways of collecting data are by:

❶ Observation: e.g. noting the colour of cars in a car park. Here you need to use a data collection sheet. This will often look like a simple tally/frequency chart (see page 58).

> Primary data is data you collect yourself.
> Secondary data is data that other people have collected.

❷ Questionnaire: Here you ask people suitable questions, e.g. 'What colour car do you drive?'

- Don't ask for information that is not needed, e.g. don't ask for a person's age if your survey doesn't need it.
- Make sure your question isn't leading (biased), e.g. never start a question 'Do you agree that ... ?'
- Allow for all possible answers. Using tick boxes is a good idea.

How many times have you been on an aeroplane?
Never ☐  1 to 2 ☐  3 to 4 ☐  5 & over ☐

## ● Two-way tables

Two-way tables show two sets of information in the one table.

➤ **Example** This two-way table shows the number of DVDs and CDs owned by a group of friends.

|  | DVDs | CDs | Total |
|---|---|---|---|
| Boys own | 2 | 9 | 11 |
| Girls own | 18 | 31 | 49 |
| Total | 20 | 40 | 60 |

Boys own 9 CDs
Girls own 18 DVDs
There is a total of 60 DVDs and CDs

1  What is wrong with this survey question?
How many dogs do you own?  None ☐  2 or more ☐

2  Complete this two-way table that shows the colours of pens owned by a group of friends.

|  | Black | Red | Blue | Total |
|---|---|---|---|---|
| Boys own | 14 |  | 11 | 26 |
| Girls own | 7 | 7 |  | 34 |
| Total | 21 | 8 | 31 | 60 |

TEST

# Frequency tables

## ● Frequency tables

Frequency tables display data that has been counted.

> **➤ Tallies** ⦀⦀⦀

Always use tallies when you are counting items of data. You should group your tallies in fives.

### ➤ Q & A

Here are the favourite colours of 20 people.

red, red, blue, green, blue, green, blue, blue, red, green, red, red, blue, green, blue, red, green, blue, red, red

Show the data in a frequency table.

**Answer**

Use a tally column to help you count.

| Colour | Tally | Frequency |
|--------|-------|-----------|
| Red | ⦀⦀⦀ ||| | 8 |
| Blue | ⦀⦀⦀ || | 7 |
| Green | ⦀⦀⦀ | 5 |
| | Total | 20 |

Write the tallies as numbers in the frequency column.

Total the numbers in the frequency column.
This helps make sure you haven't made a mistake.
The question said 20 people so this is correct.

## ● Grouping data

If you are given a long list of numbers, you can group the numbers into intervals such as $20 \leqslant n < 30$.

For example, this list:

22, 14, 15, 23, 33, 14, 37, 36, 22, 25, 31, 6, 13, 8, 23, 23, 30, 20

is shown in the frequency table.

| Number, $n$ | Tally | Frequency |
|-------------|-------|-----------|
| $0 \leqslant n < 10$ | \|\| | 2 |
| $10 \leqslant n < 20$ | \|\|\|\| | 4 |
| $20 \leqslant n < 30$ | ⦀⦀⦀ \|\| | 7 |
| $30 \leqslant n < 40$ | ⦀⦀⦀ | 5 |
| | Total | 18 |

Note: 20 belongs to $20 \leqslant n < 30$, not $10 \leqslant n < 20$.

Show this data in a frequency table (group as in the example above): 20, 12, 3, 45, 32, 9, 12, 5, 23, 25, 32, 31, 40, 32, 12, 33

TEST

# Bar charts & line graphs

Once you've got your data into a frequency table (see previous page) you can set about turning it into a nice chart or diagram.

## ● Bar charts

In a bar chart the <u>frequencies</u> from your frequency table are represented by the <u>heights of the bars</u>.

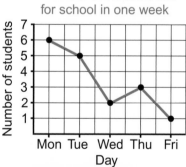

| Colour | Tally | Frequency |
|--------|-------|-----------|
| Red | ⊬⊬⊦ ‖‖ | 8 |
| Blue | ⊬⊬⊦ ‖ | 7 |
| Green | ⊬⊬⊦ | 5 |
| Total | | 20 |

Bar line graphs are similar to bar charts except lines are drawn instead of bars.

## ● Line graphs

A line graph is a set of <u>points</u> <u>joined with straight lines</u>.

This type of graph is very good for showing <u>trends</u> over periods of <u>time</u>.

The line graph on the right shows that the number of late students falls as the week goes along.

Number of students late for school in one week

The frequency table shows the number of medals that Hungary won at the 2004 Athens Olympics. Draw a pictogram (with one symbol representing 2 medals) and a bar chart to display the data.

| Medal | Frequency |
|-------|-----------|
| Gold | 8 |
| Silver | 6 |
| Bronze | 3 |

TEST

# Pie charts

## ● Drawing pie charts

### ➤ Q & A (1)

Draw a pie chart for this shopping budget.

| | |
|---|---|
| Food | £31 |
| Drinks | £12 |
| Personal hygiene | £8 |
| Cleaning products | £6 |
| Other | £3 |

### ➤ Method

❶ Add up the amounts.
❷ Calculate 360° ÷ ❶.
❸ Multiply each amount by ❷.
❹ Check the angles add to 360°.
❺ Draw and label the sectors.

**Answer**

❶ The total amount is £60.

❷ 360 ÷ 60 = 6

| Item | Amount | Angle ❸ |
|---|---|---|
| Food | £31 | 31 × 6 = 186° |
| Drinks | £12 | 12 × 6 = 72° |
| Personal hygiene | £8 | 8 × 6 = 48° |
| Cleaning products | £6 | 6 × 6 = 36° |
| Other | £3 | 3 × 6 = 18° |
| Total | £60 | 360° ❹ |

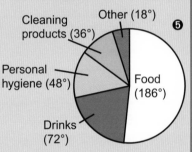

Tip: when using a 180° protractor, it is often easier to draw the small angles first.

## ● Reading pie charts

### ➤ Q & A (2)

Out of 30 students, how many watched BBC?

**Answer**

The BBC sector is 120°.

It is $\frac{120°}{360°} = \frac{1}{3}$ of the chart.

$\frac{1}{3}$ of 30 = 30 ÷ 3 = 10 students watched BBC.

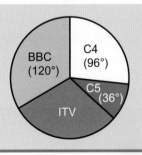

1   Show these colours on a pie chart:
    Red 40, Blue 25, Green 15, Other 10
2   Look at **Q & A (2)**. How many watched the other channels?

TEST

60

# Stem & leaf diagrams; scatter graphs

## ● Stem & leaf diagrams

These are like <u>bar charts</u>, but each bar displays the <u>actual data</u>.

### ➤ Q & A

Show this data on a stem and leaf diagram.

4, 5, 8, 12, 18, 19, 20, 22, 24, 25, 25, 26, 31, 32, 34, 36, 40, 43, 44

**Answer**

The 'stem' is the first part of the number, in this case Tens.

The 'leaf' is the rest of the number, in this case Units.

| 0 | 4 | 5 | 8 | | | |
|---|---|---|---|---|---|---|
| 1 | 2 | 8 | 9 | | | |
| 2 | 0 | 2 | 4 | 5 | 5 | 6 |
| 3 | 1 | 2 | 4 | 6 | | |
| 4 | 0 | 3 | 4 | | | |

The <u>leaves</u> should be given in <u>order of size</u>. If the original list of data had been jumbled you would have had to re-order the leaves.

Always include a key. → Key: 1 | 8 means 18

## ● Scatter graphs & correlation

This table shows some students' results for two maths tests.

| Test 1 | 5 | 8 | 9 | 11 | 15 | 17 | 19 |
|--------|---|---|---|----|----|----|----|
| Test 2 | 5 | 9 | 12 | 14 | 16 | 18 | 20 |

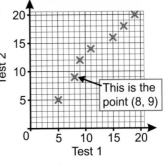

This is the point (8, 9)

You can <u>plot the points</u> on a graph – this is a <u>scatter graph</u>.

<u>Correlation</u> is a fancy way of saying whether the points are related or not:

**Positive correlation (╱)**
<u>Strong</u> if the points lie <u>close to a straight line</u>, otherwise <u>weak</u>.

**Negative correlation (╲)**
<u>Strong</u> if the points lie <u>close to a straight line</u>, otherwise <u>weak</u>.

**No correlation**
The points seem to be <u>randomly</u> positioned.

---

**a** Show the data as a scatter diagram. Describe the correlation.

**b** Show the values in a stem and leaf diagram.

| Age (years) | 1 | 6 | 4 | 4 | 10 | 3 | 8 | 7 | 9 |
|-------------|---|---|---|---|----|---|---|---|---|
| Value (£) | 45 | 18 | 28 | 24 | 4 | 37 | 10 | 17 | 9 |

TEST

# Mean, median, mode, range (1)

Mean = $\dfrac{\text{total of the values}}{\text{number of values}}$

You need to learn these.

Median = the middle value when the numbers are put in order of size

Mode = the most common value

Range = highest value – lowest value

When people talk about 'the average' they're usually referring to 'the mean'. But be careful, because the median and mode are also 'averages'.

## ➤ Q & A

Find the mean, median, mode and range of this set of data:

5, 2, 3, 1, 5, 5, 10, 2, 3

**Answer**

### Mean

The total of the values = 5 + 2 + 3 + 1 + 5 + 5 + 10 + 2 + 3 = 36
The number of values = 9 (count the numbers in the list)
So the mean = 36 ÷ 9 = 4.

### Median

Rearrange the numbers in order of size.
1, 2, 2, 3, 3, 5, 5, 5,10
The middle number is 3, so the median = 3.

### Mode

The most common value is 5 (there are three of them). So the mode = 5.

### Range

The highest value = 10 and the lowest value = 1.
So the range = 10 – 1 = 9.

> If there are an even number of values, the median is halfway between the middle two.
> e.g. the median of 2, 3, 4, 5 is (3 + 4) ÷ 2 = 3.5.

Find the mode, median, mean and range of this set of data:
5, 6, 7, 4, 4, 12, 4

TEST

Speedy Revision

# Mean, median, mode, range (2)

## ● Using the appropriate average

● The <u>mean</u> is useful as it takes all the values into account, but it can be distorted by extreme values, e.g. you wouldn't use the mean for this data: 1, 2, 2, 3, 5, 909.

● The <u>median</u> is useful when there are extreme values (as in the above example).

● The <u>mode</u> is useful when you just want the most common value, e.g. the week's best selling DVD.

## ● Finding the mean from a frequency table

The frequency table below shows the number of televisions per household in Lance's street.

| Number of TVs | 0 | 1 | 2 | 3 |
|---|---|---|---|---|
| Frequency (number of households) | 2 | 7 | 4 | 2 |

This means that 7 households have 1 TV.

The total number of TVs = $(0 \times 2) + (1 \times 7) + (2 \times 4) + (3 \times 2) = 21$
The total number of households = $2 + 7 + 4 + 2 = 15$
So the mean number of TVs per household is $21 \div 15 = 1.4$ TVs.

## ● Comparing sets of data

When comparing two sets of data you should use one of the '<u>averages</u>' <u>and</u> the <u>range</u>.

### ➤ Q & A

Jane scored a mean of 2.9 goals per game last season and had a range of $4 - 2 = 2$. David scored a mean of 3.1 goals per game and had a range of $5 - 0 = 5$. Which player would you pick for the team?

**Answer**

Although David's mean score is higher, Jane's lower range shows that she scores more consistently. So you would probably want to pick Jane, but you could pick David if you wanted a riskier strategy.

Find the mean number of TVs per household in Sarah's street:

| Number of TVs | 0 | 1 | 2 | 3 |
|---|---|---|---|---|
| Frequency (number of households) | 1 | 6 | 5 | 4 |

TEST

# Probability (1)

<u>Probability</u> is to do with the chance of something happening.

You can use words to describe different probabilities, such as: *impossible, very unlikely, unlikely, evens, likely, very likely, certain.*

Probabilities can also be given as <u>fractions or decimals</u>, but they are always <u>between 0 and 1</u>. If something has <u>probability 0</u> it <u>can't happen</u>; if it has <u>probability 1</u> it will <u>definitely happen</u>.

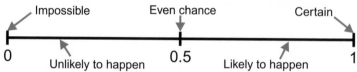

Impossible          Even chance                    Certain

0                                    0.5                                    1

    Unlikely to happen          Likely to happen

## ● Probability of something NOT happening

If the probability of something happening is $p$, then the probability of it <u>not</u> happening = $1 - p$.

> ➤ The probability of it raining tomorrow is 0.3, so the probability of it <u>not</u> raining tomorrow is $1 - 0.3 = \underline{0.7}$.

## ● Listing the outcomes of two (or more) events

### ➤ Q & A

A coin is tossed and a dice thrown. List the possible outcomes.

**Answer**

There are 2 possible outcomes for the coin: Heads (H) or Tails (T). For the dice there are 6 possible outcomes: 1, 2, 3, 4, 5 or 6.

List the outcomes systematically starting with Heads (H):

H1, H2, H3, H4, H5, H6
T1, T2, T3, T4, T5, T6          H6 is short for Heads and a 6.

Toby is going to choose a main course and dessert from the menu.

| Main course | Dessert |
|---|---|
| Spaghetti | Fruit pie |
| Pizza | Ice cream |
| | Trifle |

a   List the possible outcomes for Toby's meal.

b   The probability of Toby choosing pizza is 0.65.
   What is the probability that Toby doesn't choose pizza?

TEST

# Probability (2)

## ● Calculating probabilities

Probability of an event = $\dfrac{\text{Number of ways an event can happen}}{\text{Total number of possible outcomes}}$

### ▶ Q & A

You throw a fair dice. What is the probability of getting:
**a** a 6  **b** an even number?

**Answer**

When throwing a dice there are 6 possible outcomes: 1, 2, 3, 4, 5, 6

**a** There is only one way of getting a 6.
   $P(6) = \frac{1}{6}$

   P(6) is a short way of writing 'the probability of getting 6'.

**b** There are 3 ways of getting an even number: 2, 4 or 6.
   $P(\text{even}) = \frac{3}{6} = \frac{1}{2}$

Use the formula!

## ● Experimental probability

You can estimate probabilities from experimental data.
For example, the table shows the results when a spinner was spun 100 times:

| Colour | Red | Black | Grey |
|---|---|---|---|
| Frequency | 35 | 60 | 5 |

From the table, you can estimate that the probability that the spinner lands on black is $\frac{60}{100} = \frac{3}{5}$.

> Theoretical and experimental probabilities should be similar, but are unlikely to be the same.

For example, if you toss a coin 100 times and get heads 48 times, you shouldn't think that the coin is unfair (biased).
Increasing the number of times an experiment is repeated generally leads to better estimates of probability.

---

**1** Use a word(s) to descibe the probability that the next baby born at your local hospital will be a girl.

**2** A bag contains 2 red and 4 green beads. A bead is drawn from the bag at random. What is the probability that the bead is red?

TEST

# *Speedy* revision test (1)

These questions test the basic facts. The simple truth is that the more of them you can answer, the better you'll do in your SATs. So try them as often as you can. (The answers can be found on the pages given at the end of each question.)

**1** What do even numbers end in? What do odd numbers end in? (p4)

**2** What are the first five **a** square numbers **b** triangular numbers? (p4)

**3** What are the first five prime numbers? (p4)

**4** What is 30 squared? What is the square root of 16? (p5)

**5** Use partitioning to work out $683 - 274$. (p6)

**6** Use compensation to work out $718 - 496$. (p6)

**7** Use a written method to work out $57.3 - 1.28$. (p7)

**8** How far, and which way, should the digits move when dividing by 1000? (p8)

**9** What is the quick way to multiply something by 11? (p9)

**10** Use a written method to work out $29 \times 42$. (p10)

**11** Use a written method to work out $452 \div 6$ (there will be a remainder). (p11)

**12** What is a multiple? What is a factor? (p12)

**13** Write 20 as a product of its prime factors. (p12)

**14** How do you find the LCM of two numbers? How about the HCF? (p13)

**15** What does the symbol $\leqslant$ mean? (p14)

**16** Round 3.27 to one decimal place. (p16)

**17** Round 3.238453 to two decimal places. (p16)

**18** Which of these is correct: $-10 < -5$ or $-10 > -5$? (p17)

**19** Work out **a** $-3 + 5$ **b** $-1 - 7$. (p17)

**20** The denominator is the top of the fraction. True or false? (p18)

**21** Write $\frac{15}{45}$ in its simplest form. (p18)

**22** Complete this sentence: You can only add or subtract fractions if they have the same _____. (p19)

**23** Work out $\frac{7}{8} - \frac{3}{4}$. (p19)

**24** Write $\frac{5}{2}$ as a mixed number. (p20)

**25** Which is smaller, $\frac{3}{4}$ or $\frac{7}{12}$? (p20)

**26** Work out **a** $\frac{3}{4} \times \frac{5}{7}$ **b** $\frac{2}{9} \div \frac{3}{7}$. (p21)

**27** What is two-thirds of £60? (p21)

**28** Express £26 as a percentage of £40. (p22)

**29** Increase £20 by 17.5%. (p22)

**30** Write these as fractions: **a** 75% **b** 0.12 (p23)

**31** Simplify the ratio 50 : 100. (p24)

**32** Five apples cost 90p. How much would eight apples cost? (p24)

**33** What does BIDMAS stand for? Work out $5^2 - 2 \times (7 - 3)$. (p25)

**34** In algebra, what is a 'term'? What is an 'expression'? (p26)

**35** Multiply out the brackets in these: **a** $a(4a + b)$ **b** $-3(c - d)$ (p27)

**36** Work out $\frac{x}{3} + \frac{4x}{3}$. (p27)

**37** Solve $7x - 4 = 10$. (p28)

**38** Given that $y = 4x^3$, work out the value of $y$ when $x = 2$. (p29)

**39** What is the next term in each of these sequences?
 **a** 1, 4, 7, ... **b** 14, 10, 6, ... **c** 2, 4, 8, ... **d** 81, 27, 9, ... (p30)

# *Speedy* revision test (2)

**40** Find the *n*th term of this sequence: 6, 10, 14, 18, ... (p31)

**41 a** What is the output for this function machine when the input is 6? (p32)

$$6 \longrightarrow \boxed{\times 2} \blacktriangleright \boxed{+ 4} \longrightarrow ?$$

   **b** Write the function machine as a function using algebra. (p32)

**42** Is the *x*-axis horizontal or vertical? (p33)

**43** What should you construct before drawing a graph? (p34)

**44** How do you work out the gradient of a line? (p35)

**45** How do you know if the gradient is positive or negative? (p35)

**46** In '$y = mx + c$', what do m and c tell you? (p35)

**47** Is the line $y = b$ vertical or horizontal? (p35)

**48** What does the gradient in a distance–time graph tell you? (p36)

**49** Roughly how many litres are there in a pint? (p37)

**50** What do the angles on a straight line add up to? Angles at a point? (p40)

**51** Draw diagrams to show **a** vertically opposite angles **b** alternate angles **c** corresponding angles. (p40)

**52** What do the angles in a triangle add up to? What about a quadrilateral? (p41)

**53** What are the two formulae concerning interior and exterior angles? (p41)

**54** What is special about a *regular* polygon? (p41)

**55** If a shape can be folded so that one half fits exactly on the other, what is it said to have? (p42)

**56** What is the order of rotation symmetry of a square? (p43)

**57** When you reflect a shape in a mirror line what are not changed? (p44)

**58** Fill in the blanks. A translation moves a shape:
   ❶ a specific distance _____ or _____
   ❷ and then a specific distance _____ or _____. (p46)

**59** Complete: To describe an enlargement you give its _____ and ____ ____. (p47)

**60** What should you do first when working out the perimeter of a shape? (p48)

**61** What is the formula for the circumference of a circle? What is $\pi$? (p48)

**62** Give the formulae for the area of a triangle, rectangle, parallelogram, trapezium and a circle. (pp49–50)

**63** Sketch nets of a cuboid and a regular tetrahedron. (p51)

**64** What is the formula for the volume of a cuboid? What about a prism? (p53)

**65** What are the three things you should know about bearings? (p54)

**66** Should you start a question 'Do you agree that ... ?' in a questionnaire? (p57)

**67** Which group does 20 belong to: $10 \leqslant n < 20$ or $20 \leqslant n < 30$? (p58)

**68** What do the heights of the bars represent in a bar chart? (p59)

**69** What is a line graph good at showing? (p59)

**70** Sketch a scatter graph that shows negative correlation. (p61)

**71** How do you work out the mean, median, mode and range? (p62)

**72** The probability of something happening is 0. What does this mean? (p64)

**73** If the probability of an event happening is *p*, what's the probability of it not happening? (p64)

**74** What is the formula for calculating the probability of an event happening? (p65)

# TEST answers

**Page 4 Special numbers**
1 **a** 2, 4, 6, 8, 10, 12, 14, 16, 18, 20
   **b** 1, 3, 5, 7, 9, 11, 13, 15, 17, 19
   **c** 1, 4, 9, 16, 25, 36, 49, 64, 81, 100
   **d** 1, 3, 6, 10, 15, 21, 28, 36, 45, 55
2 **a** 32, 36, 64 **b** 49, 17, 21, 3 **c** 49, 36, 64
   **d** 21, 36, 3 **e** 17, 3

**Page 5 Squares & square roots**
1 **a** 25 **b** 121 **c** 64 **d** 1600  2 **a** 6 **b** 7 **c** 12

**Page 6 Mental strategies for + and –**
1 **a** 485 **b** 487 **c** 847 **d** 364
2 **a** 131 **b** 553 **c** 425 **d** 265

**Page 7 Written methods for + and –**
1 **a** 394 **b** 877 **c** 438 **d** 1611
2 **a** 7.89 **b** 3.84 **c** 0.16 **d** 165.83

**Page 8 Multiplying & dividing by 10, 100, ...**
1 **a** 390 **b** 8000 **c** 71 **d** 150
   **e** 42 **f** 64 **g** 1.63 **h** 1.49
2 **a** 2400 **b** 0.024 **c** 84 000 **d** 0.7

**Page 9 Mental strategies for × and ÷**
1 **a** 56 **b** 207 **c** 770 **d** 204  2 **a** 7 **b** 8 **c** 11

**Page 10 Written multiplication**
1 **a** 828 **b** 1694 **c** 44.94

**Page 11 Written division**
1 **a** 16 **b** 23 **c** 19 remainder 4
2 **a** 12.7 **b** 13.4 **c** 21.6

**Page 12 Multiples, factors & prime factors**
1 **a** 5, 10, 15, 20, 25 **b** 8, 16, 24, 32, 40
   **c** 6, 12, 18, 24, 30 **d** 9, 18, 27, 36, 45
2 **a** 1, 2, 4, 8 **b** 1, 2, 4, 8, 16, 32
   **c** 1, 2, 4, 5, 8, 10, 20, 40
3 **a** $2 \times 2 \times 3 \times 3 = 2^2 \times 3^2$
   **b** $2 \times 2 \times 3 \times 7 = 2^2 \times 3 \times 7$

**Page 13 LCM & HCF**
1 **a** 24 **b** 144  2 **a** 4 **b** 7

**Page 14 Ordering numbers**
1  34 300  **2** 33, 209, 516, 888, 1460  **3** 23.25

**Page 15 Rounding & estimating (1)**
1 **a** 80 **b** 440 **c** 1070
2 **a** 1000 **b** 1000 **c** 17 000
3  489 + 204 is roughly 500 + 200 which is
   700, so 936 must be incorrect.

**Page 16 Rounding & estimating (2)**
1 **a** 8 **b** 3 **c** 5
2 **a** 4.6 **b** 6.5 **c** 1.3 **d** 4.0
3 **a** 4.61 **b** 6.46 **c** 1.32 **d** 4.00

**Page 17 Negative numbers**
1  –10  **2** –5, –4, 0, 2, 3
3 **a** –8 + 3 = –5
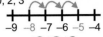
   **b** –2 – 3 = –5
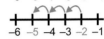

**Page 18 Fractions (1)**
1  $\frac{5}{8}$  **2 a** $\frac{2}{3}$  **b** $\frac{3}{4}$  **c** $\frac{2}{5}$

**Page 19 Fractions (2)**
1 **a** $\frac{2}{7}$  **b** $\frac{3}{5}$  **c** $\frac{8}{9}$
2 **a** $\frac{5}{9}$  **b** $\frac{2}{5}$  **c** $\frac{8}{8} = 1$
3  $\frac{2}{5}$

**Page 20 Fractions (3)**
1  $\frac{5}{3}$  **2** $3\frac{1}{3}$  **3** $\frac{1}{2}, \frac{3}{4}, \frac{7}{8}$

**Page 21 Fractions (4)**
1 **a** $\frac{10}{49}$ **b** $\frac{2}{3}$ **c** $\frac{1}{3}$ **d** $\frac{9}{14}$ **e** £22

**Page 22 Percentages**
1  20%  **2** £42  **3 a** £1200 **b** £190

**Page 23 Fractions, decimals & percentages**
1 **a** $\frac{11}{100}$ **b** $\frac{5}{100} = \frac{1}{20}$ **c** $\frac{6}{10} = \frac{3}{5}$ **d** $\frac{15}{100} = \frac{3}{20}$
2 **a** 0.7 **b** 70%
3  $\frac{35}{100} = \frac{7}{20}$

**Page 24 Ratio & proportion**
1  $\frac{2}{3}$  **2** 2 : 1  **3** £1.28

**Page 25 Calculations with brackets**
**a** 7 **b** 36.4 **c** 7 **d** 2

**Page 26 Using letters**
1  $a – 1$  **2** $n + 2$  **3 a** $2st$ **b** $u^4$
4 **a** $3t$ **b** $4n$ **c** $3y$ **d** $4x + 2$

**Page 27 Brackets & algebraic fractions**
1 **a** $4x + 8$ **b** $mn + 7m$ **c** $a^2 + ab$ **d** $–4d + 20$
2 **a** $\frac{6x}{5}$ **b** $\frac{3}{d}$

**Page 28 Equations**
1 **a** $x = 3$ **b** $x = 8$
2 ❶ $x = 4$ ❷ $x = 2$  **a** $x = 2$ **b** $x = 2$

**Page 29 Formulae & substitution**
1  $C = 25h$  **2** £200  **3 a** $a = 11$ **b** $a = 19$

**Page 30 Sequences & number patterns (1)**
1 **a** 17 **b** 48 **c** 5  **2** 14

**Page 31 Sequences & number patterns (2)**
1 **a** 7 **b** 105 **c** 205  **2 a** $3n + 4$ **b** $4n – 3$

# TEST answers

## Page 32 Functions & mappings
1  **a** 22  **b** 2  **c** $x \rightarrow 5x + 2$
2  $1 \rightarrow 7$
   $2 \rightarrow 12$
   $3 \rightarrow 17$
   $4 \rightarrow 22$

## Page 33 Coordinates
P(4, 2), Q(–3, 1), R(–3, –2), S(2, –2)

## Page 34 Straight-line graphs (1)
**a**

| $x$ | –2 | –1 | 0 | 1 | 2 |
|---|---|---|---|---|---|
| $y = 3x + 2$ | –4 | –1 | 2 | 5 | 8 |

**b**
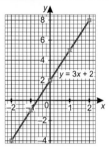

## Page 35 Straight-line graphs (2)
$y = 5x + 4$

## Page 36 Real-life graphs
1  The train starts at station A and travels to station C at a constant speed. The train waits at station C before travelling to station B. The train waits at station B and then travels more slowly back to station A.
2  5

## Page 37 Units of measurement
1  **a** 200 cm  **b** 6 cm
2  **a** Roughly 30 g  **b** Roughly 450 g

## Page 38 Appropriate units & reading scales
1  **a** metres  **b** litres  **c** grams
2  **a** 35  **b** 68

## Page 39 Estimating & measuring angles
1  **a** Between 70° & 80°  **b** Between 160° & 170°
2  **a** 75°  **b** 165°

## Page 40 Angles & parallel lines
$a = 65°$, $b = 56°$, $c = d = 124°$, $e = 38°$, $f = 128°$

## Page 41 Polygons
1  49°
2  **a** Interior = 90°, exterior = 90°
   **b** Interior = 120°, exterior = 60°

## Page 43 Symmetry & properties of shapes (2)
1  **a** **i** 2 **ii** 2  **b** **i** 1 **ii** 1  **c** **i** 3 **ii** 3
2  For example:

## Page 44 Reflection
**a**

**b**
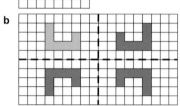

## Page 45 Rotation
**a**   **b**

## Page 46 Translation
1
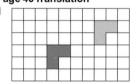

2
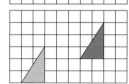

## Page 47 Enlargement
1
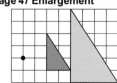

# TEST answers

**2**

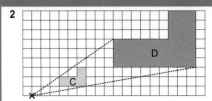

## Page 48 Perimeter & circumference
**1  a** 28 cm  **b** 28 cm
**2**  50.24 cm (using π = 3.14)

## Page 50 Area of 2-D shapes (2)
**a** 42 cm²  **b** 33 cm²  **c** 18 cm²  **d** 27 m²
**e** 200.96 cm²  **f** 153.86 cm² (using π = 3.14)

## Page 51 Nets & 3-D shapes; plans & elevations
**1  a** 6 faces, 12 edges, 8 vertices
   **b** 5 faces, 9 edges, 6 vertices
**2**  For example:

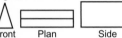

Front     Plan          Side

The 11 nets of a cube are:

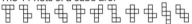

## Page 52 Surface area
**a** 76 cm²  **b** 84 cm²

## Page 53 Volume
**a** 40 cm³  **b** 36 cm³

## Page 54 Bearings & scale drawings
**1  a** 090°  **b** 270°  **2**  100 km

## Page 56 Constructions & loci (2)
**3**

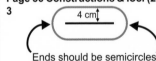

4 cm

Ends should be semicircles

## Page 57 Collecting data & two-way tables
**1**  There is no option for 1 dog.
**2**

|          | Black | Red | Blue | Total |
|----------|-------|-----|------|-------|
| Boys own | 14    | 1   | 11   | 26    |
| Girls own| 7     | 7   | 20   | 34    |
| Total    | 21    | 8   | 31   | 60    |

## Page 58 Frequency tables

| Number, *n*   | Tally | Frequency |
|---------------|-------|-----------|
| 0 ≤ n < 10    | III   | 3         |
| 10 ≤ n < 20   | III   | 3         |
| 20 ≤ n < 30   | III   | 3         |
| 30 ≤ n < 40   | HHI   | 5         |
| 40 ≤ n < 50   | II    | 2         |
|               | Total | 16        |

## Page 59 Bar charts & line graphs

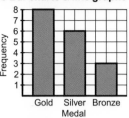

## Page 60 Pie charts
**1**

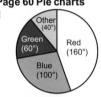

**2**  ITV: 9 students
      C4: 8 students
      C5: 3 students

## Page 61 Stem & leaf diagrams; scatter graphs
**a**

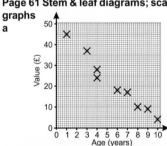

The graph shows strong negative correlation, i.e. value decreases as age increases.

**b**

| 0 | 4 9     |
|---|---------|
| 1 | 0 7 8   |
| 2 | 4 8     |
| 3 | 7       |
| 4 | 5       |

Key: 1 | 8 means 18

## Page 62 Mean, median, mode, range (1)
Mode = 4, median = 5, mean = 6, range = 8

## Page 63 Mean, median, mode, range (2)
1.75 TVs

## Page 64 Probability (1)
**a**  spaghetti & fruit pie, pizza & fruit pie
     spaghetti & ice cream, pizza & ice cream
     spaghetti & trifle, pizza & trifle
**b**  0.35

## Page 65 Probability (2)
**1**  Evens, even chance or fifty-fifty  **2**  $\frac{2}{6} = \frac{1}{3}$

# Index

# Index

Speedy Revision